CREATIVE WRITING IN SCIENCE

ACTIVITIES THAT INSPIRE

CREATIVE WRITING IN SCIENCE

ACTIVITIES THAT INSPIRE

KATIE COPPENS

National Science Teachers Association

Arlington, Virginia

Claire Reinburg, Director
Wendy Rubin, Managing Editor
Rachel Ledbetter, Associate Editor
Amanda O'Brien, Associate Editor
Donna Yudkin, Book Acquisitions Coordinator

ART AND DESIGN
Will Thomas Jr., Director
Himabindu Bichali, Graphic Designer, cover and
    interior design

PRINTING AND PRODUCTION
Catherine Lorrain, Director

NATIONAL SCIENCE TEACHERS ASSOCIATION
David L. Evans, Executive Director
David Beacom, Publisher

1840 Wilson Blvd., Arlington, VA 22201
www.nsta.org/store
For customer service inquiries, please call 800-277-5300.

NSTA is committed to publishing material that promotes the best in inquiry-based science education. However, conditions of actual use may vary, and the safety procedures and practices described in this book are intended to serve only as a guide. Additional precautionary measures may be required. NSTA and the authors do not warrant or represent that the procedures and practices in this book meet any safety code or standard of federal, state, or local regulations. NSTA and the authors disclaim any liability for personal injury or damage to property arising out of or relating to the use of this book, including any of the recommendations, instructions, or materials contained therein.

Library of Congress Cataloging-in-Publication Data
Names: Coppens, Katie, 1979-
Title: Creative writing in science : activities that inspire / Katie Coppens.
Description: Arlington, VA : National Science Teachers Association, [2016] |
  Includes bibliographical references and index.
Identifiers: LCCN 2015046551 (print) | LCCN 2016007839 (ebook) | ISBN 9781941316351 (print) |
ISBN 9781681400006 | ISBN 9781681400006 (e-book)
Subjects: LCSH: English language--Study and teaching (Secondary) | Creative writing (Secondary education) |
Science--Study and teaching (Secondary) | Interdisciplinary approach in education.
Classification: LCC PE1066 .C59 2016 (print) | LCC PE1066 (ebook) | DDC 808/.0420712--dc23
LC record available at *http://lccn.loc.gov/2015046551*

CONTENTS

Introduction

Life Science Activities

Earth and Space Science Activities

CONTENTS

Engineering and Physical Science Activities

Appendixes

ABOUT THE
AUTHOR

Katie Coppens is an award-winning middle school language arts and science teacher. As a teacher of both subjects, she uses creative writing throughout her science curriculum to engage students and assess their knowledge. Since her career began in 2001, she has had a variety of teaching experiences, ranging from teaching a self-contained third-grade classroom to teaching high school English and biology while volunteering in Tanzania. She lives in Maine with her husband, who is a high school biology teacher, and their two children. For more information on the author and her publications, please visit *www.katiecoppens.com*.

Source: Peggy Becksvoort

INTRODUCTION

CHAPTER 1

WHY WRITE CREATIVELY IN SCIENCE?

Creative writing allows students to apply their knowledge in an imaginative way. To engage students and meet a range of learning styles, this book demonstrates a variety of writing forms—from fictional narrative essays to poetry to comics.

By assessing students through creative writing, you will see new strengths in your students and have a better understanding of their writing skills and science knowledge. Each student's approach to an assignment may be different, which allows students to take pride in the individuality of their final product.

Before integrating writing into the content area, you must ensure that students have a solid foundation of the knowledge and vocabulary of a given unit. Assignments throughout the book could serve as formative assignments if you implement them while teaching your unit. The assignments could also be summative assignments if you use them after a concept has been taught or at the end of your unit.

The activities and rubrics were written to meet a range of grade level and teacher needs. Depending on your class or grade level, the same assignment may be used by one teacher as a class activity, by another teacher as homework, and by a third teacher as his or her final assignment for a unit.

To help meet the needs of teachers and students, each assignment supports the *Common Core State Standards* and the *Next Generation Science Standards*. At least one model of writing is also included for each activity to help students understand expectations and to inspire their own creativity. More examples of student models can be found on the NSTA Press extras page at *www.nsta.org/ creativewritinginscience*.

CHAPTER 2

SCORING STUDENT WRITING

Teachers have a range of comfort levels when scoring the actual writing within a piece, especially writing fluency and conventions. Therefore, two different rubrics are included for each assignment. One rubric scores the application of science knowledge and vocabulary. The other rubric scores the science content, language use, and conventions. Scoring the mechanics and style of writing benefits students by reinforcing what they are learning in language arts, by showing them that writing is important across the content areas, and by making them more accountable for the quality of their writing.

The two rubrics that follow (Tables 2.1 and 2.2 [p. 6]) illustrate the typical scoring criteria in this book. The rubrics are applicable across grade levels and are written in a purposeful, open-ended style to encourage students to be creative and take risks.

Table 2.1 Poetry Rubric: Scoring for Science and Writing Content

AREA	1 DOES NOT MEET EXPECTATIONS	2 PARTIALLY MEETS EXPECTATIONS	3 MEETS EXPECTATIONS	4 EXCEEDS EXPECTATIONS
SCIENCE CONTENT	The poem lacks information and shows that you do not understand the concepts of this unit, *or* the poem shows consistent misconceptions.	The poem shows correct understanding but lacks details, *or* poem demonstrates some minor misconceptions.	The poem includes appropriate and detailed information that shows an overall understanding of the unit.	The poem has thorough and detailed information, showing an understanding of the unit that is distinguished (very strong).
LANGUAGE USE	Writing flow and spelling errors make the poem difficult to understand.	Writing flow and spelling errors distract the reader.	The spelling is correct, and the flow of the poem is smooth to the reader.	The spelling, flow, and style of the poem are distinguished (very strong).

Table 2.2 Narrative Rubric: Scoring for Science and Writing Content

AREA	1 DOES NOT MEET EXPECTATIONS	2 PARTIALLY MEETS EXPECTATIONS	3 MEETS EXPECTATIONS	4 EXCEEDS EXPECTATIONS
SCIENCE CONTENT	The narrative lacks information and shows that you do not understand the concepts of this unit, *or* the narrative shows consistent misconceptions.	The narrative shows correct understanding but lacks details, *or* narrative demonstrates some minor misconceptions.	The narrative includes appropriate and detailed information that shows an overall understanding of the unit.	The narrative has thorough and detailed information, showing an understanding that is distinguished (very strong).
USE OF SCIENCE VOCABULARY	The narrative does not include enough science vocabulary to show understanding, *or* the narrative uses terms incorrectly.	The narrative includes some relevant science vocabulary, but it needs more to adequately show knowledge.	The narrative consistently uses science vocabulary in the appropriate context.	The narrative uses extensive and appropriate science vocabulary throughout.
WRITING FLUENCY	Writing flow and errors in sentence structure make the narrative difficult to understand.	Writing flow and errors in sentence structure writing distract the reader.	The sentence structure is correct and the flow of writing is smooth to the reader.	The sentence structure, flow, and style of writing are distinguished (very strong).
CONVENTIONS	Spelling, capitalization, and punctuation errors make the narrative difficult to understand.	Spelling, capitalization, and punctuation errors make the narrative difficult to understand.	Spelling, capitalization, punctuation, and grammar are mostly *or* all correct.	The spelling, capitalization, punctuation, and grammar are distinguished (very strong).

CHAPTER 3

CHAPTER FORMAT

Each chapter is organized with a consistent structure. The first few pages are background information for the teacher and include sections on the following topics:

Writing Styles

This section explains the writing styles that will be incorporated in an assignment, such as narrative writing, poetry, or argumentative writing.

Purpose

This section provides the reason for giving the assignment.

Overview

This section summarizes the assignment.

Language Arts Connections

This section includes instructional methods to help improve the quality of student writing. For example, narrative writing may emphasize the importance of voice or point of view, whereas another lesson may focus on personification or the proper letter-writing format.

Differentiation Strategies

This section discusses teaching methods, alternative assignments, or extensions to meet the needs of all learners in your classroom. Potential misconceptions are also addressed.

Connections to the *Next Generation Science Standards*

This section explains how a specific assignment supports the *Next Generation Science Standards* for grades 3–12.

Applications to Other Science Areas

Each assignment models a different method of creative writing. This section gives ideas for other topics in science for which a specific style of creative writing could be applied.

The next section of each chapter is intended for students.

Assignment

Students are given this page when an assignment is introduced. It includes an overview of the assignment and a scoring rubric. For every activity, two versions of each assignment sheet are provided: one with a rubric that scores just the science content and another with a rubric that scores the science content and the writing. Teachers can choose whichever rubric they are most comfortable using.

Graphic Organizers

The prewriting process is an important step in allowing students to successfully integrate science and writing. A variety of methods are provided to help students brainstorm and organize their science knowledge before they begin their writing.

Models

Each assignment provides one or more models, which are written at a seventh- or eighth-grade level. Because of the age range of the book, you will need to adjust the model according to the grade level taught. For example, when there is a narrative prompt, third graders may be expected to write one paragraph, whereas high school students may be expected to write an essay. More examples of student models can be found on the NSTA Press extras page at *www.nsta.org/creativewritinginscience*.

A benefit of showing a model when an assignment is introduced is that it can improve students' understanding of expectations; however, the downside is that a model can stifle creativity. An alternative method could be to have students first complete a graphic organizer to plan their writing. This organizer allows students develop some of their ideas before seeing a model.

Saving student models from year to year (with the names removed) to serve as exemplars can also be beneficial. In addition, you can use the models as a class activity in which students look at their rubric and score the models in various areas. Having a range of exemplars, from a score of 1 to a score of 4, can help students better understand the rubric and the expectations of an assignment.

LIFE
SCIENCE
ACTIVITIES

CHAPTER 4

EVERY TREE IS A CHARACTER

Writing Styles

Narrative, descriptive

Purpose

Students will work individually to apply forestry knowledge and vocabulary to a piece of fictional writing.

Overview

For this activity, students write a fictional story about a tree. It may help to have students first observe a tree, with a focus on the evidence of human or natural impact and the sensory details they experience at the site of the tree. To encourage application of knowledge from the unit, ask students to underline or italicize key vocabulary in their final piece.

Language Arts Connections

Discuss character and how conflict affects characters. Students should have various types of conflict occur in their tree story to engage the reader and show their knowledge of natural and human impact. *Personification* is a literary device that gives human characteristics to something that is not human. This device helps create imagery and engages the reader in the story. Point of view and voice can also make stories more effective. There is one first-person point of view model and one third-person point of view model. When you compare the models' opening sentences, you see that they set very different tones for the story. For example, this sentence has a playful feel: "Bob, the birch, is not an ordinary tree; he is more like a cat with nine lives." While this sentence reads more like a fable: "I don't remember the day the wind carried my seed from the pinecone, for it was many, many sunrises ago."

Differentiation Strategies

An alternative assignment is for students to draw circles to represent the years of a tree's life. Students can label the rings with a number and write a sentence for what the tree may have experienced during that year. Students who need more of a challenge could focus on explaining photosynthesis and cellular respiration.

Although personification is an effective literary device, it could potentially lead to misconceptions for some students. It may be helpful to emphasize that students are writing a fictional piece and that trees do not actually have the emotions portrayed in the story.

Connections to the *Next Generation Science Standards*

- **3-LS1.1:** Develop models to describe that organisms have unique and diverse life cycles but all have in common birth, growth, reproduction, and death.

- **3-LS4-2:** Use evidence to construct an explanation for how the variations in characteristics among individuals of the same species may provide advantages in surviving, finding mates, and reproducing.

- **3-LS4-3:** Construct an argument with evidence that in a particular habitat some organisms can survive well, some survive less well, and some cannot survive at all.

- **5-LS1-1:** Support an argument that plants get the materials they need for growth chiefly from air and water.

- **MS-LS1-5:** Construct a scientific explanation based on evidence for how environmental and genetic factors influence the growth of organisms.

- **MS-LS1-6:** Construct a scientific explanation based on evidence for the role of photosynthesis in the cycling of matter and flow of energy into and out of organisms.

- **MS-LS2-3:** Develop a model to describe the cycling of matter and flow of energy among living and nonliving parts of an ecosystem.

- **MS-LS2-4:** Construct an argument supported by evidence that changes to physical or biological components of an ecosystem affect populations.

- **HS-LS1-5:** Use a model to illustrate how photosynthesis transforms light energy into stored chemical energy.

- **HS-LS2-3:** Construct and revise an explanation based on empirical evidence for the cycling of matter and flow of energy in aerobic and anaerobic conditions.

- **HS-LS2-5:** Develop a model to illustrate the role of photosynthesis and cellular respiration in the cycling of carbon among the biosphere, atmosphere, hydrosphere, and geosphere.

- **HS-LS4-5:** Evaluate the evidence supporting claims that changes in environmental conditions may result in (1) increases in the number of individuals of some species, (2) the emergence of new species over time, and (3) the extinction of other species.

Applications to Other Science Areas

You could have students write a fictional story from the perspective of a water droplet going through the water cycle or a story from the point of view of a comet that describes our solar system.

Name: _____ Date: _____

Every Tree Is a Character

Write a fictional piece that tells the story of a tree. Be sure to show your knowledge of forestry and ecology. You can write the story from the first-person point of view (from the perspective of the tree) or the third-person point of view (from the perspective of a narrator).

> Vocabulary I could use from this unit in my writing includes the following:
>
>
>
>
>
>
>
>
>

You will be scored according to the following rubric:

AREA	1 DOES NOT MEET EXPECTATIONS	2 PARTIALLY MEETS EXPECTATIONS	3 MEETS EXPECTATIONS	4 EXCEEDS EXPECTATIONS
SCIENCE CONTENT	The narrative lacks information and shows that you do not understand forestry/ecology concepts, *or* narrative shows consistent misconceptions.	The narrative shows correct understanding of forestry or ecology concepts but lacks details, *or* narrative demonstrates some minor misconceptions.	The narrative includes appropriate and detailed information about forestry/ecology concepts.	The narrative has thorough and detailed information, showing an understanding of forestry/ecology concepts that is distinguished (very strong).
USE OF SCIENCE VOCABULARY	The narrative does not include enough science vocabulary to show understanding, *or* the narrative uses terms incorrectly.	The narrative includes some relevant science vocabulary, but it needs more to adequately show knowledge.	The narrative consistently uses science vocabulary in the appropriate context.	The narrative uses extensive and appropriate science vocabulary throughout.

Use the organizer on page 16 to plan your story.

Name: _____ Date: _____

Every Tree Is a Character

Write a fictional piece that tells the story of a tree. Be sure to show your knowledge of forestry and ecology. You can write the story from the first-person point of view (from the perspective of the tree) or the third-person point of view (from the perspective of a narrator).

Vocabulary I could use from this unit in my writing includes the following:

You will be scored according to the following rubric:

AREA	1 DOES NOT MEET EXPECTATIONS	2 PARTIALLY MEETS EXPECTATIONS	3 MEETS EXPECTATIONS	4 EXCEEDS EXPECTATIONS
SCIENCE CONTENT	The narrative lacks information and shows that you do not understand forestry/ecology concepts, *or* narrative shows consistent misconceptions.	The narrative shows correct understanding of forestry or ecology concepts but lacks details, *or* narrative demonstrates some minor misconceptions.	The narrative includes appropriate and detailed information about forestry *or* ecology concepts.	The narrative has thorough and detailed information, showing an understanding of forestry or ecology concepts that is distinguished (very strong).
USE OF SCIENCE VOCABULARY	The narrative does not include enough science vocabulary to show understanding, *or* the narrative uses terms incorrectly.	The narrative includes some relevant science vocabulary, but it needs more to adequately show knowledge.	The narrative consistently uses science vocabulary in the appropriate context.	The narrative uses extensive and appropriate science vocabulary throughout.
WRITING FLUENCY	Writing flow and errors in sentence structure make the narrative difficult to understand.	Writing flow and errors in sentence structure distract the reader.	The sentence structure is correct, and the flow of writing is smooth to the reader.	The sentence structure, flow, and style of writing are distinguished (very strong).
CONVENTIONS	Spelling, capitalization, and punctuation errors make the narrative difficult to understand.	Spelling, capitalization, and punctuation errors distract the reader.	The spelling, capitalization, punctuation, and grammar are mostly *or* all correct.	The spelling, capitalization, punctuation, and grammar are distinguished (very strong).

Use the organizer on page 16 to plan your story.

Name: _____ Date: _____

Every Tree Is a Character: Observations

Sit by a tree and write observations of what you see and experience. Organize your observations by *Environmental or Sensory Details* (Do you see cars? Hear birds? Smell pine trees? What does the wind feel like?) and *Impact* (Are there trees cut down nearby? Roads nearby? Nests? Branches broken off?).

ENVIRONMENTAL OR SENSORY DETAILS	IMPACT (HUMAN AND NATURAL)

Sketch of a tree

Name: _____ Date: _____

Every Tree Is a Character: Organizer

From whose point of view will the story be told?_____

Where is the tree located? _____

List three ways the tree's environment has changed over its life:

1. _____

2. _____

3. _____

Write a first sentence that captures the reader's attention:

_____

_____

Fill in the boxes with a sequence of events that could have happened to the tree:

Every Tree Is a Character: Model

Vocabulary I could use from this unit in my writing includes the following:

Abiotic Adaptation Biotic Canopy Clear-cutting Climax Community Competition Cones Coniferous Deciduous Decomposer Ecosystem Even-aged stand Food web Forest floor Hardwood Harvest Immature Leaves Lichen Mature Niche Photosynthesis Pioneer species Population Sapling Seedling Shade intolerant Shade tolerant Shelterwood Snag Softwood Succession Understory Watershed

Bob, the birch, is not an ordinary tree; he is more like a cat with nine lives. There have been eight events that *could* have caused Bob to no longer be the tree you see today. The first happened when he was just a seed. He blew in the wind and landed less than three meters from a river. If he had landed in the water, he would have quickly become fish food. But he didn't; instead, he landed on fertile ground with a beautiful view.

The second event was when he was just a *seedling*. A deer was munching on grass and almost ate Bob. But, she didn't because a lighting strike distracted her.

Next, Bob was growing very close to another sapling and *competition* began between them. His *adaptations* were stronger so he was able to claim the land and capture the Sun's energy through the process of *photosynthesis*.

As Bob got bigger, thunder and lightning returned. Because he was not the largest tree in the area, the lightning hit an older, taller tree instead.

A windstorm occurred when Bob's trunk had not yet grown thick and sturdy. He held tight with all of his might, and just when his roots were about to lift from the ground, the wind changed direction.

His sixth save occurred when a beaver was gathering wood for his dam. Bob was just the right size for the beaver: not too big and not too small. Just as the beaver was about to bite into Bob's *hardwood*, he noticed a coyote lurking in the woods. You see, in the *food web*, coyotes eat beavers, so the beaver's instincts told him to run away fast.

As Bob grew bigger, a beetle landed on a leaf. This wasn't just any beetle, it was a bronze beech borer, who has larvae that can kill birch trees. Just as the bronze beech borer was about to burrow into Bob, it was eaten by a bird.

Then today, just as a furniture maker was about to swing his axe and chop down Bob, he remembered that maple is an even harder *deciduous* tree. Bob let out a big sigh of oxygen and felt relief that he was able to live another day.

Name: _____ Date: _____

Every Tree Is a Character: Model

Vocabulary I could use from this unit in my writing includes the following:

Abiotic Adaptation Biotic Canopy Clear-cutting Climax Community Competition Cones Coniferous Deciduous Decomposer Ecosystem Even-aged stand Food web Forest floor Hardwood Harvest Immature Leaves Lichen Mature Niche Photosynthesis Pioneer species Population Sapling Seedling Shade intolerant Shade tolerant Shelterwood Snag Softwood Succession Understory Watershed

I don't remember the day the wind carried my seed from the pine*cone*, for it was many, many sunrises ago. I wish I could count my rings, but I can't. I must rely on my memory and the memories of those around me.

You see, long ago, when my seed found fertile ground, a forest of trees surrounded me. Stories of the past whispered with the wind, and I loved to hear *mature* trees describe how our home had changed. First, there were the *pioneer species*. Then, through *succession*, more trees began to grow. The *shade intolerant* species were drawn to the open Sun and their seeds quickly began to sprout. Many of these were *deciduous* trees who proudly waved their *leaves*. They created a *canopy* of shade for trees like me, the *shade tolerant*, who prefer to not be in the open Sun. We waited for the day the *climax* species would come, like the hemlock and fir, and claim our forest. These were the best days of my life, when I felt the warm wind on my bark and squirrels scurrying on my needles, and our forest felt like a *community*.

Over time, we continued to grow and became crowded. It was hard for us all to get the energy we needed. The trees and I were having a healthy *competition* for sunlight by stretching our branches high and wide, when I heard the sound—the sound I will never forget—a chainsaw.

Each day, more and more trees were taken. Now, only a few of us remain, spread out so far from each other that the wind cannot carry our words. I do not know what the future holds for us, but I hope that more seeds will come. I dream of the day we will be a *community* once again, and I can pass on the story of our home to the *saplings* that grow beneath my outstretched branches.

Every Tree Is a Character: Model of Tree Rings

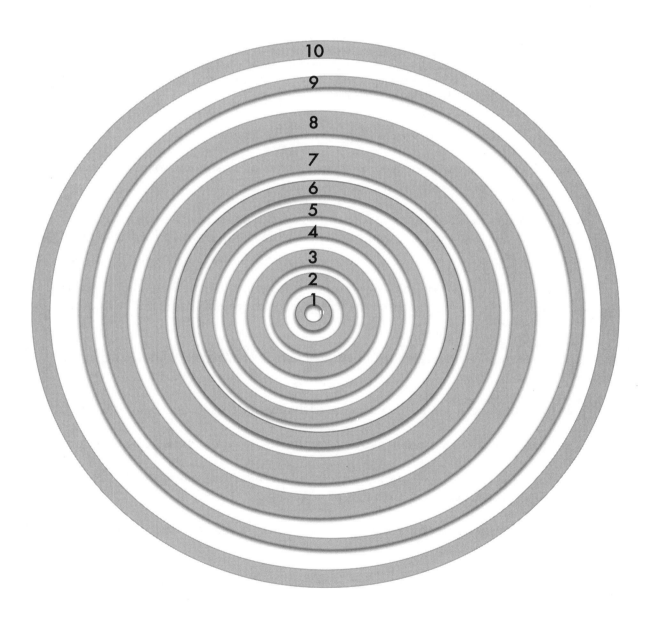

Every Tree Is a Character: Model of Tree Rings

Vocabulary I could use from this unit in my writing includes the following:

Abiotic Adaptation Biotic Canopy Clear-cutting Climax Community Competition Cones Coniferous Deciduous Decomposer Ecosystem Even-aged stand Food web Forest floor Hardwood Harvest Immature Leaves Lichen Mature Niche Photosynthesis Pioneer species Population Sapling Seedling Shade intolerant Shade tolerant Shelterwood Snag Softwood Succession Understory Watershed

Year 1: The seed grew from a *seedling* to a small *deciduous sapling*.

Year 2: The *sapling* experienced *competition* with other *saplings* for the nutrients in the soil. It expanded its roots underground.

Year 3: A squirrel died near the tree and was eaten by *decomposers*, which is part of the *food web*. This put nutrients in the ground, which helped the tree grow.

Year 4: There was a drought. The amount of water in a habitat is an *abiotic* factor; this abiotic factor caused the tree to have less growth compared with other years.

Year 5: A nearby *snag* fell on the *forest floor*, which created a lot of nutrients in the soil.

Year 6: The *deciduous* tree's *leaves* captured the Sun's energy through *photosynthesis*.

Year 7: The healthy *ecosystem* allowed the tree to thrive and grow a lot this year.

Year 8: The tree had a big enough *canopy* that a *shade-tolerant seedling* started to grow next to it, which is part of *succession*.

Year 9: The tree was hit by lightning, which is an *abiotic* factor, but survived. There was some damage to the tree.

Year 10: *Clear-cutting* occured in the forest, and all the trees were cut down.

CHAPTER 5

POSTCARD FROM A BIOME

Writing Styles

Narrative, descriptive

Purpose

Students will work individually to apply knowledge and vocabulary of a biome to a piece of fictional writing.

Overview

For this activity students write a postcard to show their knowledge of the organisms and landscape within a biome. On the blank side of an index card, students draw a picture to show visually what the biome looks like. On the other side, students write a message that contains information about the biome.

Language Arts Connections

Discuss the proper letter-writing format. Remind students to begin with "Dear_____," and to sign the postcard "Sincerely, _____," or another salutation.

After brainstorming on the organizer, have students circle the five most important concepts and vocabulary words that will show their knowledge of the biome. Because writing space is limited, the assignment makes them choose the most important information to put on their postcards.

Differentiation Strategies

You can help students who struggle to start their writing by giving them an opening sentence, such as the one in the model: "I have been in the _____ for six days, and I can't believe all that I have seen." If drawing is not a strength for students, they could always make a collage on the cover of their postcard. Emphasize capturing the colors of the biome and including at least one organism.

Some students may feel that their writing style is limited on a postcard. They could be given the option to write a letter instead. Rather than including a picture, they can use their words to fully describe what the landscape looks like.

Connections to the *Next Generation Science Standards*

- **3-LS4-3:** Construct an argument with evidence that in a particular habitat some organisms can survive well, some survive less well, and some cannot survive at all.

- **MS-LS2-2:** Construct an explanation that predicts patterns of interactions among organisms across multiple ecosystems.
- **MS-LS2-4:** Construct an argument supported by empirical evidence that changes to physical or biological components of an ecosystem affect populations.

Applications to Other Science Areas

You could have students write a postcard from a planet. They could explain how long the journey was to the planet and what the environment is like there. Or, students could write a postcard from Europe and describe how the metric system is used.

Name: _____ Date: _____

Postcard From a Biome

You will create a postcard to show your understanding of one of the world's biomes. On the front, draw a picture of the biome that shows what a typical landscape looks like. On the back, write details of your trip that show your understanding of the habitat and the organisms that live there. Be sure to use vocabulary from this unit.

VOCABULARY (What vocabulary can you use from the unit?)	LANDSCAPE (What does the land look like?)	ORGANISMS (What plants and animals do you see?)

You will be scored according to the following rubric:

AREA	1 DOES NOT MEET EXPECTATIONS	2 PARTIALLY MEETS EXPECTATIONS	3 MEETS EXPECTATIONS	4 EXCEEDS EXPECTATIONS
SCIENCE CONTENT	The postcard lacks information and shows that you do not understand the biome, *or* postcard shows consistent misconceptions.	The postcard shows correct understanding but lacks details about the biome, *or* postcard demonstrates some minor misconceptions.	The postcard includes appropriate and detailed information that shows an overall understanding of the biome.	The postcard has thorough and detailed information about the biome, showing an understanding that is distinguished (very strong).
USE OF SCIENCE VOCABULARY	The postcard does not include enough science vocabulary to show understanding, *or* the postcard uses terms incorrectly.	The postcard includes some relevant science vocabulary, but it needs more to adequately show knowledge.	The postcard consistently uses science vocabulary in the appropriate context.	The postcard uses extensive and appropriate science vocabulary throughout.

Use the organizer on page 25 to plan your postcard.

Name: _____ Date: _____

Postcard From a Biome

You will create a postcard to show your understanding of one of the world's biomes. On the front, draw a picture of the biome that shows what a typical landscape looks like. On the back, write details of your trip that show your understanding of the habitat and the organisms that live there. Be sure to use vocabulary from this unit.

VOCABULARY (What vocabulary can you use from the unit?)	LANDSCAPE (What does the land look like?)	ORGANISMS (What plants and animals do you see?)

You will be scored according to the following rubric:

AREA	1 DOES NOT MEET EXPECTATIONS	2 PARTIALLY MEETS EXPECTATIONS	3 MEETS EXPECTATIONS	4 EXCEEDS EXPECTATIONS
SCIENCE CONTENT	The postcard lacks information and shows that you do not understand the biome, *or* postcard shows consistent misconceptions.	The postcard shows correct understanding but lacks details about the biome, *or* postcard demonstrates some minor misconceptions.	The postcard includes appropriate and detailed information that shows an overall understanding of the biome.	The postcard has thorough and detailed information about the biome, showing an understanding that is distinguished (very strong).
USE OF SCIENCE VOCABULARY	The postcard does not include enough science vocabulary to show understanding, *or* the postcard uses terms incorrectly.	The postcard includes some relevant science vocabulary, but it needs more to adequately show knowledge.	The postcard consistently uses science vocabulary in the appropriate context.	The postcard uses extensive and appropriate science vocabulary throughout.
WRITING FLUENCY	Writing flow and errors in sentence structure make the postcard difficult to understand.	Writing flow and errors in sentence structure distract the reader.	The sentence structure is correct, and the flow of writing is smooth to the reader.	The sentence structure, flow, and style of writing are distinguished (very strong).
CONVENTIONS	Spelling, capitalization, and punctuation errors make the narrative difficult to understand.	Spelling, capitalization, and punctuation errors distract the reader.	The spelling, capitalization, punctuation, and grammar are mostly *or* all correct.	The spelling, capitalization, punctuation, and grammar are distinguished (very strong).

Use the organizer on page 25 to plan your postcard.

Name: _____ Date: _____

Postcard From a Biome: Organizer

On the front, draw a picture of the biome. Include colors that represent the biome and at least one organism. For the rough draft, draw a quick sketch.

On the back, write details about
what you see (organisms, landscape).

_____

_____

_____

Postcard From a Biome: Model for a Tropical Rain Forest

Dear _____,

I have been in the Amazon rain forest for six days, and I can't believe all that I have seen. The temperature during the day has been about 30°C (86°F), while at night it has been about 21°C (70°F). We are sleeping in tents below the high *canopy* of trees. Each night, I hear *nocturnal* creatures such as the *Wallace's flying frog*. Its croaking lulls me to sleep. During the day, I'm in awe of the beautiful green color. It is so green because it rains around two and a half meters (100 inches) a year here! My favorite plants are the *epiphytes* that grow up and around the trees to get to the light. It broke my heart when I learned that people are cutting down the rain forest for *logging*. When I get home, I will research how to help save this beautiful biome.

Sincerely,

_____

CHAPTER 6

TRAVEL BLOG ABOUT THE DIGESTIVE SYSTEM

Writing Styles

Narrative, descriptive

Purpose

Students will work individually to apply knowledge and vocabulary of the human digestive system to a piece of fictional writing.

Overview

Students show their knowledge of the digestive system by writing a travel blog from the perspective of a piece of food as it journeys through the human body.

Language Arts Connections

Explain that a blog is a website that is written with a casual, friendly style and is updated regularly. There are many examples of blogs, such as for cooking, reviewing books, or, in this case, sharing travel experiences. Blogs are typically full of personal reactions and often have humor. It would be helpful for students to see some examples of travel blogs online.

When looking at blogs, focus on various styles and types of voice. The food that is journeying down the digestive tract should take on a distinctive voice to help the reader connect to the character. The character is a piece of food, so the voice could match the type of food it is. For example, a piece of tofu would have a different personality than a candy bar. It is recommended that students first write the science content in their blog and then focus on the voice.

To prevent too much silliness for the final leg of the trip (the rectum), give students an example of how a blog could end or provide them with an appropriate ending. The model demonstrates this as follows: "At last … I saw the light! I knew I had spent 35 hours changing forms, but finally I could see what I looked like. As I felt a cool splash of water, I realized that I was about to take a whole new journey. The last thing I remember hearing before my next trip began was the resounding echo of a 'FLUSH!'"

Differentiation Strategies

Giving students a specific item of food for this assignment may help. For example, foods with a high sugar content could lead to a more in-depth explanation of the pancreas and the impact on the bloodstream. This assignment can also give students the opportunity to connect an understanding of the digestive system to nutrition.

An alternative assignment could be for students to write a tweet for each step of their journey through the digestive system. A tweet is limited to 140 characters. That limit causes students to summarize the most important scientific details of the digestive tract.

Although personification is an effective literary device, it could potentially lead to misconceptions for some students. It may be helpful to emphasize that students are writing a fictional piece and that food does not actually have the emotions portrayed in the story.

Connections to the *Next Generation Science Standards*

- **5-LS2-1:** Develop a model to describe the movement of matter among plants, animals, decomposers, and the environment.

- **MS-LS1-7:** Develop a model to describe how food is rearranged through chemical reactions forming new molecules that support growth or release energy as this matter moves through an organism.

- **MS-LS1-3:** Use argument supported by evidence for how the body is a system of interacting subsystems composed of groups of cells.

Applications to Other Science Areas

You could have students complete a blog for a water droplet's journey through the water cycle or for energy through a food chain.

Name: _____ Date: _____

Travel Blog About the Digestive System

You will write a travel blog about a journey through each part of the digestive system. Be sure to demonstrate your knowledge of each part of the system with vocabulary from this unit. Use the organizer to decide what key information you will incorporate into your writing.

You will be scored according to the following rubric:

AREA	1 DOES NOT MEET EXPECTATIONS	2 PARTIALLY MEETS EXPECTATIONS	3 MEETS EXPECTATIONS	4 EXCEEDS EXPECTATIONS
SCIENCE CONTENT	The blog lacks information and shows that you do not understand digestive system concepts, *or* the blog shows consistent misconceptions.	The blog shows correct understanding of the digestive system but lacks details, *or* blog includes some minor misconceptions.	The blog includes appropriate and detailed information that shows an overall understanding of the digestive system.	The blog has thorough and detailed information, showing an understanding of the digestive system that is distinguished (very strong).
USE OF SCIENCE VOCABULARY	The blog does not use terms properly, *or* not enough vocabulary is used to show understanding.	The blog includes some relevant science vocabulary, but it needs more to adequately show knowledge.	The blog consistently uses relevant science vocabulary in the appropriate context.	The blog uses extensive and appropriate science vocabulary throughout.

Use the organizer on pages 31–33 to plan your blog.

Name: _____ Date: _____

Travel Blog About the Digestive System

You will write a travel blog about a journey through each part of the digestive system. Be sure to demonstrate your knowledge of each part of the system with vocabulary from this unit. Use the organizer to decide what key information you will incorporate into your writing.

You will be scored according to the following rubric:

AREA	1 DOES NOT MEET EXPECTATIONS	2 PARTIALLY MEETS EXPECTATIONS	3 MEETS EXPECTATIONS	4 EXCEEDS EXPECTATIONS
SCIENCE CONTENT	The blog lacks information and shows that you do not understand digestive system concepts, *or* the blog shows consistent misconceptions.	The blog shows correct understanding of the digestive system but lacks details, *or* blog includes some minor misconceptions.	The blog includes appropriate and detailed information that shows an overall understanding of the digestive system.	The blog has thorough and detailed information, showing an understanding of the digestive system that is distinguished (very strong).
USE OF SCIENCE VOCABULARY	The blog does not use terms properly, *or* not enough vocabulary is used to show understanding.	The blog includes some relevant science vocabulary, but it needs more to adequately show knowledge.	The blog consistently uses relevant science vocabulary in the appropriate context.	The blog uses extensive and appropriate science vocabulary throughout.
WRITING FLUENCY	Writing flow and errors in sentence structure make the blog difficult to understand.	Writing flow and errors in sentence structure distract the reader.	The sentence structure is correct, and the flow of writing is smooth to the reader.	The sentence structure, flow, and style of writing are distinguished (very strong).
CONVENTIONS	Spelling, capitalization, and punctuation errors make the narrative difficult to understand.	Spelling, capitalization, and punctuation errors distract the reader.	The spelling, capitalization, punctuation, and grammar are mostly *or* all correct.	The spelling, capitalization, punctuation, and grammar are distinguished (very strong).

Use the organizer on pages 31–33 to plan your blog.

Name: _____ Date: _____

Travel Blog About the Digestive System: Organizer

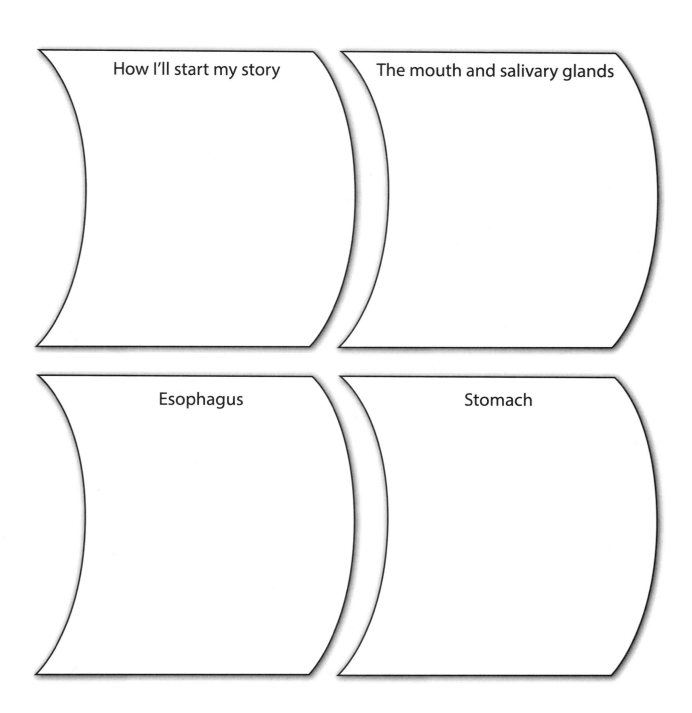

How I'll start my story

The mouth and salivary glands

Esophagus

Stomach

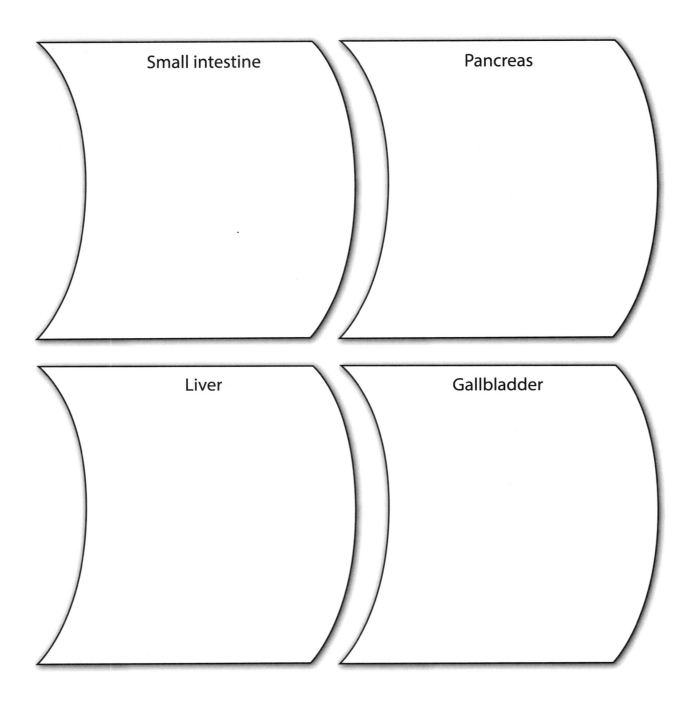

Small intestine

Pancreas

Liver

Gallbladder

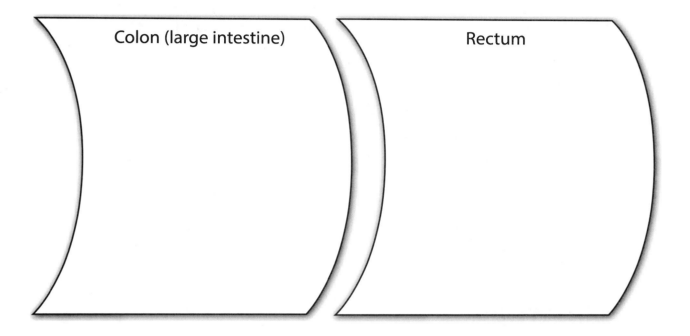

Colon (large intestine)

Rectum

Travel Blog About the Digestive System: Model

Popcorn's Journey Through the Digestive Tract

It all began when I was plucked from the bag that I was happily resting in. I remember the brief moment that I flew free from his hand and quickly approached his open mouth. Many people think a piece of popcorn's journey ends here, but it was just the beginning of one of the greatest adventures of my life. This is the blog of what occurred over my 35-hour, 9-meter (30-foot) journey through the *digestive tract*.

Stop 1: The Mouth and Salivary Glands

I first landed on a wonderful warm, soft, pink couch of some sort. I believe it is called a *tongue*. I was only there for a moment before everything quickly changed. I was pounded again and again by numerous hard, white *teeth*. For every one of those brutal objects on top, there was one just as hard on the bottom. I was pummeled until I was no longer me. Instead, everywhere I looked I saw small pieces of myself. It was quite disturbing at first, but I had only a small glimpse of light to see that I had become a soft form of food called a *bolus*. In an instant, all the pieces of me were washed away by a warm, wet wave of *saliva*. It felt kind of nice after the barbaric act that had just occurred.

Stop 2: Esophagus

I next journeyed quickly down a long, dark, slimy slide of some sort. Almost instantly, I passed through the *pharynx* and could feel something called a *trachea*, which had air flowing through it. I could hear it whizzing by me as I felt pushing in all directions. *Peristalsis* occurred, which is a series of *contractions* from all around. Muscles in the *esophagus* shoved me deeper into a large, hollow container of some sort. This part of the trip was almost 20 centimeters (8 inches) long!

Stop 3: Stomach

This stop proved to be the most unpleasant container one would ever experience. The smell quickly hit me from the *enzymes* and *acid* that washed over me. I stayed there until I was broken down into a much smaller form, called *chyme*, and surrounded by *digestive juices*.

Stop 4: Small Intestine

I next found myself on a winding path that continued for an astonishing 7 meters (more than 20 feet)! More *enzymes* came at me, causing me to break down even further. As I felt myself get smaller, I noticed that it became easier to continue my journey through the *duodenum, jejunum,* and *ileum. Secretions* were released that helped make my journey feel like I was on a slippery slide. It smelled terrible, but it was kind of fun to twist and turn in all directions. The closest that I had ever experienced to this was when all the kernels started to pop in the bag just a few hours ago and I was thrown in all different directions. As I moved, I brushed against small, soft bristles of *cilia* that pushed me along. I also felt my *nutrients* being taken from me through the *mucosa*. They were absorbed into the soft *intestine walls*. From there, they had their own journey into the *bloodstream*.

Stop 5: Pancreas

A highlight from my trip in the *small intestine* was the *pancreas*. I didn't actually go through it, but it sure affected my trip! It was at the beginning of the winding path and it released *enzymes* and *pancreatic juice*. What came from it was really powerful! The *pancreas* helped break down the butter that was on me and break down my *carbohydrates. Insulin* is also produced here, which helps the body use *sugar* from food.

Stop 6: Liver and Gallbladder

Much like the *pancreas*, I didn't travel through the *liver*, but it was right there with the *gallbladder*. The *gallbladder* was the smelliest part of the journey; it stores all the *bile* that breaks down things such as *fat* in the *small intestine*. The *liver* and *pancreas* both work really hard to keep this guy healthy!

Stop 7: Colon (Large Intestine)

Eight hours from the start of my journey, the little bit of me that remained entered the *cecum*, which is part of another large pathway. All the best parts of me had been taken by this point to give *energy* to the man who ate me. The *bloodstream* took away my *sugars, vitamins,* and *salt*. Other parts were absorbed, and all that was left was my "*waste*." I was in a *liquid state* at first, but as I traveled through the *ascending colon*, then the *transverse colon*, and finally the *descending colon,* I changed into a *solid state*. With each turn through the winding path, more water was removed. I combined with the *waste* of other foods and changed into my final *solid form*. I kept noticing *bacteria* along the way, which made me realize the end was near. But, it was not until I hit the *sigmoid colon* that I knew my journey was almost over.

Stop 8: Rectum

At last … I saw the light! I knew I had spent 35 hours changing forms, but finally I could see what I looked like. As I felt a cool splash of water, I realized that I was about to take a whole new journey. The last thing I remember hearing before my next trip began was the resounding echo of a "FLUSH!"

CHAPTER 7

PHYTOPLANKTON COMIC

Writing Styles

Comic, graphic novella

Purpose

Students will work individually to apply knowledge and vocabulary about phytoplankton to a comic.

Overview

Students show the life cycle of phytoplankton through a comic, which focuses on both storytelling and visual representations. Through this comic, students demonstrate the important role that phytoplankton play in the ocean's food web and the production of our Earth's oxygen. Students will also demonstrate their knowledge of photic zones.

Language Arts Connections

Comics and graphic novels are both visual ways of telling a story. For both of these forms of writing, well-chosen pictures are an essential part of creating the setting. The setting students choose is important because it allows you to see their understanding.

Narration or dialogue helps with the comic's structure and organization. Much like other forms of writing, comics have a story arc with a beginning, middle, and end. Whether through narration or dialogue, the text gives the story voice and demonstrates knowledge of content and vocabulary from the unit. To relieve students of the pressure to be funny in their comic, emphasize that the author's purpose is to teach his or her audience the importance of phytoplankton.

Differentiation Strategies

To get students started on this assignment, bring in comics from the newspaper to model a plot and the organization of a beginning, middle, and end. Students can also explore how dialogue and narration are effectively used to convey the message of the story. It may benefit students to receive the vocabulary from the unit that you would like to see them use accurately in their comic. Students who need more of a challenge can focus on explaining photosynthesis and cellular respiration.

Some students may feel challenged by the artistic aspect of this assignment. In that case, they may prefer to use clip art images or websites that allow them to make comics online. Students who are strong artists may prefer to make a graphic novella (a short graphic novel).

Connections to the *Next Generation Science Standards*

- **3-LS1.1:** Develop models to describe that organisms have unique and diverse life cycles but all have in common birth, growth, reproduction, and death.
- **5-PS3-1:** Use models to describe that energy in animals' food (used for body repair, growth, motion, and to maintain body warmth) was once energy from the Sun.
- **5-LS1-1:** Support an argument that plants get the materials they need for growth chiefly from air and water.
- **5-LS2-1:** Develop a model to describe the movement of matter among plants, animals, decomposers, and the environment.
- **MS-LS1-6:** Construct a scientific explanation based on evidence for the role of photosynthesis in the cycling of matter and flow of energy into and out of organisms.
- **MS-LS2-3:** Develop a model to describe the cycling of matter and flow of energy among living and nonliving parts of an ecosystem.
- **HS-LS1-5:** Use a model to illustrate how photosynthesis transforms light energy into stored chemical energy.
- **HS-LS2-3:** Construct and revise an explanation based on empirical evidence for the cycling of matter and flow of energy in aerobic and anaerobic conditions.
- **HS-LS2-5:** Develop a model to illustrate the role of photosynthesis and cellular respiration in the cycling of carbon among the biosphere, atmosphere, hydrosphere, and geosphere.

Applications to Other Science Areas

You could have students complete this assignment for anything in science that has a visual component, such as the process of a sedimentary rock forming, one of Newton's laws, or the function of sound waves.

Name: _____ Date: _____

Phytoplankton Comic

Your assignment is to show your understanding of phytoplankton through a comic. Be sure to include phytoplankton's life cycle and the important effect(s) that phytoplankton have on our planet. Visuals in the comic should give a clear sense of setting, whereas the text in the comic should demonstrate your understanding of vocabulary from this unit.

Facts about phytoplankton and *vocabulary* I could use from this unit in my writing include the following:

You will be scored according to the following rubric:

AREA	1 DOES NOT MEET EXPECTATIONS	2 PARTIALLY MEETS EXPECTATIONS	3 MEETS EXPECTATIONS	4 EXCEEDS EXPECTATIONS
VISUAL AND SCIENCE CONTENT	The comic lacks visuals and shows that you do not understand phytoplankton or its role in the ocean's food web.	The visuals show some correct understanding of phytoplankton but lack details, *or* visuals demonstrate some minor misconceptions.	The comic includes appropriate visuals that show an overall understanding of phytoplankton.	The visuals show an understanding of phytoplankton that is distinguished (very strong).
USE OF SCIENCE VOCABULARY	The comic does not include enough science vocabulary to show understanding, *or* the comic uses terms incorrectly.	The comic includes some relevant science vocabulary, but it needs more to adequately show knowledge.	The comic consistently uses science vocabulary in the appropriate context.	The comic uses extensive and appropriate science vocabulary throughout.

Use the organizer on page 41 to plan the events of your comic.

Name: _____ Date: _____

Phytoplankton Comic

Your assignment is to show your understanding of phytoplankton through a comic. Be sure to include phytoplankton's life cycle and the important effect(s) that phytoplankton have on our planet. Visuals in the comic should give a clear sense of setting, whereas the text in the comic should demonstrate your understanding of vocabulary from this unit.

Facts about phytoplankton and *vocabulary* I could use from this unit in my writing include the following:

You will be scored according to the following rubric:

AREA	1 DOES NOT MEET EXPECTATIONS	2 PARTIALLY MEETS EXPECTATIONS	3 MEETS EXPECTATIONS	4 EXCEEDS EXPECTATIONS
VISUAL AND SCIENCE CONTENT	The comic lacks visuals and shows that you do not understand phytoplankton or its role in the ocean's food web.	The visuals show some correct understanding of phytoplankton but lack details, *or* visuals demonstrate some minor misconceptions.	The comic includes appropriate visuals that show an overall understanding of phytoplankton.	The visuals show an understanding of phytoplankton that is distinguished (very strong).
USE OF SCIENCE VOCABULARY	The comic does not include enough science vocabulary to show understanding, *or* the comic uses terms incorrectly.	The comic includes some relevant science vocabulary, but it needs more to adequately show knowledge.	The comic consistently uses science vocabulary in the appropriate context.	The comic uses extensive and appropriate science vocabulary throughout.
CONVENTIONS	Spelling, capitalization, and punctuation errors make the comic difficult to understand.	Spelling, capitalization, and punctuation errors distract the reader.	Spelling, capitalization, punctuation, and grammar are mostly *or* all correct.	Spelling, capitalization, punctuation, and grammar are distinguished (very strong).

Use the organizer on page 41 to plan the events of your comic.

Name: _____ Date: _____

Phytoplankton Comic: Organizer

_____

In what setting will the phytoplankton be? _____

_____

Where in the water are phytoplankton found? _____

_____

_____

How do phytoplankton form? _____

_____

_____

What role/importance do phytoplankton have? _____

_____

_____

_____

_____

_____

In the comic cells on page 42, make a plan for what information you will show in your comic. You may need more or fewer comic cells than provided.

Planning Your Comic

Phytoplankton Comic: Model

CHAPTER 8

MOTIVATIONAL SPEECH BY A PART OF A CELL

Writing Styles

Persuasive, argumentative

Purpose

Students will work individually to apply knowledge and vocabulary about plant or animal cells to a piece of persuasive writing.

Overview

Students write a motivational speech from the point of view of one part of a cell, such as the mitochondria or nucleus. Students read their speeches in front of the class, pretending that the rest of the class is also that part of a cell, with the goal of trying to motivate the other cell parts. In doing so, students explain the important functions of the cell part they represent.

Language Arts Connections

Persuasive or argumentative writing is when you try to convince your audience that your claim is correct. Argumentative writing emphasizes the evidence to support your claim and the acknowledgment of a counterclaim. Persuasive writing includes more emotions and personal opinion; however, it is important that the writing also presents evidence to show knowledge. Regardless of which form of writing students choose, they must remember that speech writing includes another purpose, which is to engage listeners.

Speeches should include an opening statement with a main point (this is the claim, thesis, or controlling idea), a body with supporting details, and a conclusion. To keep speeches interesting, students can include a grabber—such as humor, rhetorical questions, or anecdotes—to pull the audience in. Speeches should be written from the first-person point of view, so it may help students to know that the pronouns they should be using are "I" and "we."

Differentiation Strategies

You can differentiate by assigning parts of the cell to students, depending on the difficulty. You can also provide the vocabulary that you would like to see students use correctly in their speeches. Students who need more of a challenge can focus on the interactions between systems and the way the systems all function together to support life.

Students should write their speeches and practice reading them. Eye contact is an important part of public speaking. To help with this, students may want to write bulleted talking points on note cards instead of writing the entire speech out. For example, rather than writing an opening of: "Hello, cell walls. I stand before you today to remind you why we are the most important part of the plant cell. Without us, the plant cell would have no structure, no shape." A bulleted talking point may say, "Important because of structure and shape." This method causes students to make eye contact, which helps the speaker engage the audience. With practice, some students may even be able to give their speeches without any resources in front of them.

Connections to the *Next Generation Science Standards*

- **4-LS1-1:** Construct an argument that plants and animals have internal and external structures that function to support survival, growth, behavior, and reproduction.

- **MS-LS1-2:** Develop and use a model to describe the function of a cell as a whole and ways parts of a cell contribute to the function.

- **MS-LS1-3:** Use argument supported by evidence for how the body is a system of interacting subsystems composed of groups of cells.

- **HS-LS1-2:** Develop and use a model to illustrate the hierarchical organization of interacting systems that provide specific functions within multicellular organisms.

- **HS-LS1-7:** Use a model to illustrate that cellular respiration is a chemical process whereby the bonds of food molecules and oxygen molecules are broken and the bonds in new compounds are formed, resulting in a net transfer of energy.

Applications to Other Science Areas

You could have students complete a motivational speech for various categories of consumers (carnivores, omnivores, herbivores, decomposers, etc.), for the different human body systems, or for the eight forms of energy.

Name: _____ Date: _____

Motivational Speech by a Part of a Cell

Your assignment is to write a motivational speech from the point of view of a part of a cell. Pretend you are speaking to an audience of that same cell part. Motivate your audience members to understand their significance to the whole cell's function and the contribution they make to the organism's survival. You will read this speech in front of the class, so you should engage and interest your audience!

Part of cell = _____

You will be scored according to the following rubric:

AREA	1 DOES NOT MEET EXPECTATIONS	2 PARTIALLY MEETS EXPECTATIONS	3 MEETS EXPECTATIONS	4 EXCEEDS EXPECTATIONS
SCIENCE CONTENT	The speech lacks information about the cell part and shows that you do not understand the concepts of this unit, *or* speech shows consistent misconceptions.	The speech shows correct understanding but lacks details about the cell part's functions, *or* speech demonstrates some minor misconceptions.	The speech includes appropriate and detailed information about the cell part that shows an overall understanding.	The speech has thorough and detailed information about the cell part, showing an understanding that is distinguished (very strong).
USE OF SCIENCE VOCABULARY	The speech does not include enough science vocabulary to show understanding, *or* the speech uses terms incorrectly.	The speech includes some relevant science vocabulary, but it needs more to adequately show knowledge.	The speech consistently uses science vocabulary in the appropriate context.	The speech uses extensive and appropriate science vocabulary throughout.
ORAL PRESENTATION	The speech is unprepared and unclear.	Parts of the speech are unclear because of a lack of organization, volume, or eye contact.	The presentation is organized and has consistent eye contact and a clear speaking style. The motivation comes across well.	The speech has the "wow" factor, is very motivational, and really captures the class's attention!

Use the organizer on page 49 to help structure your speech.

Name: _____ Date: _____

Motivational Speech by a Part of a Cell

Your assignment is to write a motivational speech from the point of view of a part of a cell. Pretend you are speaking to an audience of that same cell part. Motivate your audience members to understand their significance to the whole cell's function and the contribution they make to the organism's survival. You will read this speech in front of the class, so you should engage and interest your audience!

Part of cell = _____

You will be scored according to the following rubric:

AREA	1 DOES NOT MEET EXPECTATIONS	2 PARTIALLY MEETS EXPECTATIONS	3 MEETS EXPECTATIONS	4 EXCEEDS EXPECTATIONS
SCIENCE CONTENT	The speech lacks information about the cell part and shows that you do not understand the concepts of this unit, or speech shows consistent misconceptions.	The speech shows correct understanding but lacks details about the cell part's functions, or speech demonstrates some minor misconceptions.	The speech includes appropriate and detailed information about the cell part that shows an overall understanding.	The speech has thorough and detailed information about the cell part, showing an understanding that is distinguished (very strong).
USE OF SCIENCE VOCABULARY	The speech does not include enough science vocabulary to show understanding, or the speech uses terms incorrectly.	The speech includes some relevant science vocabulary, but it needs more to adequately show knowledge.	The speech consistently uses science vocabulary in the appropriate context.	The speech uses extensive and appropriate science vocabulary throughout.
ORAL PRESENTATION	The speech is unprepared and unclear.	Parts of the speech are unclear because of a lack of organization, volume, or eye contact.	The presentation is organized and has consistent eye contact and a clear speaking style. The motivation comes across well.	The speech has the "wow" factor, is very motivational, and really captures the class's attention!
WRITING FLUENCY	Writing flow and errors in sentence structure make the speech difficult to understand.	Writing flow and errors in sentence structure distract the reader.	The sentence structure is correct, and the flow of writing is smooth to the reader.	The sentence structure, flow, and style of writing are distinguished (very strong).
CONVENTIONS	Spelling, capitalization, and punctuation errors make the speech difficult to understand.	Spelling, capitalization, and punctuation errors distract the reader.	The spelling, capitalization, punctuation, and grammar are mostly or all correct.	The spelling, capitalization, punctuation, and grammar are distinguished (very strong).

Use the organizer on page 49 to help structure your speech.

Motivational Speech by a Part of a Cell: Organizer

Introduction: Pull the listener in and have a main point about why this cell part matters.

Body: Include evidence of why the cell part is important to the whole cell and the organism.

Conclusion: End with a lasting inspirational message about the cell part's importance.

Motivational Speech by a Part of a Cell: Model (Cell Wall)

Hello, cell walls. I stand before you today to remind you why we are the most important part of the plant cell. Without us, the plant cell would have no *structure* and no shape. We are the protectors of the cell—both *strong* and *flexible*. *Cellulose* allows us to stand like armed guards defending a fortress: We decide what can and cannot pass. We stop *toxins* from entering, allow *waste* to escape, and permit *nutrients* to come through. We are the exit and the entrance. We are the door and the wall. What is a home without walls? And what is a cell without us? It is weak, vulnerable, and unstable. Alone, we are important, but when you put us all together … *We* are unstoppable. So stand strong, my friends, and know that through our structure and support, plant life will continue.

Introduction

Hello, cell walls. I stand before you today to remind you why we are the most important part of the plant cell. Without us, the plant cell would have no structure and no shape. We are the protectors of the cell—both strong and flexible.

Body

Cellulose allows us to stand like armed guards defending a fortress: We decide what can and cannot pass. We stop toxins from entering, allow waste to escape, and permit nutrients to come through. We are the exit and the entrance. We are the door and the wall. What is a home without walls? And what is a cell without us? It is weak, vulnerable, and unstable.

Conclusion

Alone, we are important, but when you put us all together … *We* are unstoppable. So stand strong, my friends, and know that through our structure and support, plant life will continue.

EARTH AND SPACE SCIENCE ACTIVITIES

CHAPTER 9

GROUP POEM: EARTH'S HISTORY

Writing Style

Poem

Purpose

Students will apply knowledge and vocabulary from a period of time in Earth's history to a poem. Students will combine their individual efforts to make one collaborative class poem.

Overview

For this activity, students write a poem about an eon, era, period, or epoch. First, cut up the poem topics (pp. 57–59) and give one to each student. They are labeled with the time period, years it occurred, and what number they are in the sequence. When it is time to share, have students sit in order. Reading the poems aloud gives the story of Earth's history, while celebrating the individual contribution of students and the collaboration of the class as a whole.

Language Arts Connections

You can teach students a variety of poetry forms. Many students will be drawn to the haiku because of its simple 5-7-5 syllable format. However, it is important to emphasize that the 17 syllables be used effectively. Students could also try this form of poetry but write multiple haikus to show the events of their time period. Other students may choose an acrostic poem in which you spell the word out and write a poem using the letters. However, this form of poetry often leads to a word being used because it starts with the right letter and not because it is the best choice.

For free verse, use the model provided to show how line breaks in the poem create pauses and how repetition can create rhythm. Stanzas are used much like paragraphs to show a transition in the writing. Remind students that poems do not have to rhyme. If they choose to rhyme, their poem can benefit from following a pattern such as ABAB, ABBA, AABA, or ABCB. For example, a stanza with an AABB rhyming pattern would read as follows:

Warm, flowing lava began to pool
Then, at last, the rock did cool
Water vapor formed a sea
While underwater vents let air flow free

Differentiation Strategies

Having a variety of options for poem format is an example of differentiation. Another method is to give students one of the mass extinction categories, rather than a time period. Those categories are simpler for students to understand because the emphasis is on the extinctions that occurred and the specific event(s) that caused them, rather than having a variety of events to choose from in a large time period.

Some students may need help pronouncing words in their poem. It can benefit students to rewrite their poem with words broken into syllables or sounds, such as "Pale-e-o-zo-ic." This strategy will help students feel more confident when reading in front of the class.

Connections to the *Next Generation Science Standards*

- **3-LS4-1:** Analyze and interpret data from fossils to provide evidence of the organisms and the environment from which they lived long ago.

- **4-ESS1-1:** Identify evidence from patterns in rock formations and fossils in rock layers to support an explanation for changes in a landscape over time.

- **MS-ESS1-4:** Construct a scientific explanation based on evidence from rock strata for how the geologic time scale is used to organize Earth's 4.6-billion-year-old history.

- **MS-LS4-1:** Analyze and interpret data for patterns in the fossil record that document the existence, diversity, extinction, and change of life forms throughout the history of life on Earth under the assumption that natural laws operate today as in the past.

- **HS-ESS1-6:** Apply scientific reasoning and evidence from ancient Earth materials, meteorites, and other planetary surfaces to construct an account of Earth's formation and early history.

Applications to Other Science Areas

You could apply this assignment to any topic in which students can have an individual part that comes together to show an entire linear concept. For example, you could have students write poems for the phases of the Moon or various parts of a food web.

Name: _____ Date: _____

Group Poem: Earth's History

Earth's history is broken into eons, eras, periods, and epochs. Your assignment is to write a poem that shows your knowledge of the events of a given period of time. When everyone is finished, the class will read the poems in chronological order to learn the major events of Earth's history. The organizer below will help you write your poem.

I am responsible for _____, which will be read _____.

This occurred from _____ to _____ years ago.

Major events that occurred during this time include the following:

You will be scored according to the following rubric:

AREA	1 DOES NOT MEET EXPECTATIONS	2 PARTIALLY MEETS EXPECTATIONS	3 MEETS EXPECTATIONS	4 EXCEEDS EXPECTATIONS
SCIENCE CONTENT	The poem lacks correct information and shows that you do not understand the major events of this time period, *or* the poem shows consistent misconceptions.	The poem includes accurate information but does not focus on the major events of the time period, *or* the poem demonstrates some minor misconceptions.	The poem includes accurate information that shows an overall understanding of the time period's major events.	The poem includes detailed and accurate information, showing an understanding of the time period that is distinguished (very strong).

Name: _____ Date: _____

Group Poem: Earth's History

Earth's history is broken into eons, eras, periods, and epochs. Your assignment is to write a poem that shows your knowledge of the events of a given period of time. When everyone is finished, the class will read the poems in chronological order to learn the major events of Earth's history. The organizer below will help you write your poem.

I am responsible for _____, which will be read _____.

This occurred from _____ to _____ years ago.

Major events that occurred during this time include the following:

You will be scored according to the following rubric:

AREA	1 DOES NOT MEET EXPECTATIONS	2 PARTIALLY MEETS EXPECTATIONS	3 MEETS EXPECTATIONS	4 EXCEEDS EXPECTATIONS
SCIENCE CONTENT	The poem lacks correct information and shows that you do not understand the major events of this time period, *or* the poem shows consistent misconceptions.	The poem includes accurate information but does not focus on the major events of the time period, *or* the poem demonstrates some minor misconceptions.	The poem includes accurate information that shows an overall understanding of the time period's major events.	The poem includes detailed and accurate information, showing an understanding of a time period that is distinguished (very strong).
LANGUAGE USE	Writing flow and spelling errors make the poem difficult to understand.	Writing flow and spelling errors distract the reader.	The spelling is correct, and the flow of the poem is smooth to the reader.	The spelling, flow, and style of the poem are distinguished (very strong).

Group Poem: Earth's History

(Cut and hand the strips out to students.)

(1) Precambrian Time: 4.6 billion to 541 million years ago

(2) Hadean Time: 4.6 billion to 4 billion years ago

(3) Archaen Eon: 4 billion to 2.5 billion years ago

(4) Proterozoic Eon: 2.5 billion to 541 million years ago

(5) Phanerozoic Eon: 541 million years ago to the present

(6) Paleozoic Era: 541 million to 252 million years ago

(7) Cambrian period: 541 million to 485 million years ago

(8) Ordovician Period: 485 million to 443 million years ago

(9) Silurian Period: 443 to 419 million years ago

(10) Devonian Period: 419 million to 359 million years ago

(11) Carboniferous Period: 359 to 299 million years ago

(12) Permian Period: 299 million to 252 million years ago

(13) Mesozoic Era: 252 million to 66 million years ago

(14) Triassic Period: 252 million to 201 million years ago

(15) Jurassic Period: 201 million to 145 million years ago

(16) Cretaceous Period: 145 million to 66 million years ago

(17) Cenozoic Era: 66 million years ago to the present

(18) Paleogene Period: 66 million to 23 million years ago

(19) Paleocene Epoch: 66 million to 56 million years ago

(20) Eocene Epoch: 56 million to 33.9 million years ago

(21) Oligocene Epoch: 33.9 million to 23 million years ago

(22) Neogene Period: 23 million to 2.58 million years ago

(23) Miocene Epoch: 23 million to 5.3 million years ago

(24) Pilocene Epoch: 5.3 million to 2.58 million years ago

(25) Quaternary Period: 2.58 million years ago to the present

(26) Pleistocene Epoch: 2.58 million to 11,700 years ago

(27) Holocene Epoch: 11,700 years ago to present day

Mass Extinctions

(8.5) Ordovician-Silurian Mass Extinction: 443 million years ago

(10.5) Late Devonian Mass Extinction: 359 million years ago

(12.5) Permian Mass Extinction: 252 million years ago

(14.5) Triassic-Jurassic Mass Extinction: 201 million years ago

(16.5) Cretaceous-Tertiary Mass Extinction: 66 million years ago

Group Poem: Earth's History: Model for Precambrian Time

Precambrian Time Haiku

Whirling, hot gases
Lava cools, then water flows
Bacteria live

Precambrian Time Free Verse

For most of Earth's past
It felt alone in the emptiness of space
Spinning, waiting, hoping
Unaware of what may come

It began over four billion years ago
With hot gases and lava
Colliding, combining, cooling
Unaware of what may come

As rock formed
Layers built up, creating a crust
A crucial crust that was hardening
Unaware of what may come

Slowly, water vapor united
Eventually, forming our seas
Vents release bubbles, floating freely
Unaware of what may come

Water and oxygen create life
Simple bacteria grow, mate, evolve
Leading to multicellular organisms
That grow, mate, and evolve …

Unaware of what may come.

CHAPTER 10

PRESENTING ... THE ROCK CYCLE!

Writing Styles

Narrative, poem, skit, play, song

Purpose

Students will work individually or in a group to apply knowledge and vocabulary about the rock cycle to a piece of fictional writing.

Overview

In this lesson, students become the teachers of the class by presenting a creative writing piece that demonstrates the rock cycle.

Language Arts Connections

It will help students to think about the setting for each stage of the rock cycle. Doing so will help students explore the conditions in which rock forms. For example, limestone forms in warm, shallow seas, whereas shale can form in swampy areas.

For poetry, use the model provided to show how line breaks in the poem create intentional pauses. Remind students that poems do not have to rhyme, but they should have rhythm. If students do choose to rhyme, they should follow a pattern such as ABAB, AABB, ABBA, or a more complex one such as the following stanza, which has an AABBCC rhyming pattern:

> Igneous rocks are born from fire
> A phase as magma, it does require
> Some harden slowly below the ground
> Others harden quickly as a lava mound
> My favorite is obsidian with its black hue
> But pumice and granite are quite nice too

Differentiation Strategies

Offering choices in how students would like to use creative writing to teach the class leads to differentiation. The assignment also allows students to get another idea approved by their teacher. This alternative format could be anything from a comic to a Claymation video.

Some students may benefit from having the arrows on the graphic organizer filled in with terms such as *melting* and *compacting*. Students who need more of a challenge can also focus on the effects of the geosphere, biosphere, and hydrosphere on the rock cycle.

Metamorphic rocks have the most potential for causing student misconceptions and may not be developmentally appropriate for all age groups. This same assignment could be given for telling the story of a specific sedimentary or igneous rock. Students could bring a sedimentary or igneous rock to school and brainstorm how that rock formed. Allowing students to hold the rock may help this assignment feel less abstract. Metamorphic rocks could be an option for students who have shown a strong understanding of concepts in the unit.

Connections to the *Next Generation Science Standards*

- **4-ESS1-1:** Identify evidence from patterns in rock formations and fossils in rock layers to support an explanation for changes in a landscape over time.

- **5-ESS2-1:** Develop a model using an example to describe ways the geosphere, biosphere, hydrosphere, or atmosphere interact.

- **MS-ESS2-1:** Develop a model to describe the cycling of Earth's materials and the flow of energy that drives this process.

- **MS-ESS2-2:** Construct an explanation based on evidence for how geoscience processes have changed Earth's surface at varying time and spatial scales.

- **HS-ESS2-5:** Plan and conduct an investigation of the properties of water and its effects on Earth materials and surface processes.

Applications to Other Science Areas

You could have students teach the class about the process of photosynthesis, the states of matter, or the cause of seasons.

Name: _____ Date: _____

Presenting ... the Rock Cycle!

Your assignment is to use creative writing to teach the class about the rock cycle. You can work independently or in a small group (the more minds involved, the higher the expectations). Your goal is to show your understanding in a clear, creative way. Here are some options for how you could teach the class:

*Write a poem. *Write a short story. *Perform a skit (you must provide a script).

*Write a song. *Choose another idea that is *approved* by your teacher.

Vocabulary I could use from this unit in my writing includes the following:

You will be scored according to the following rubric:

AREA	1 DOES NOT MEET EXPECTATIONS	2 PARTIALLY MEETS EXPECTATIONS	3 MEETS EXPECTATIONS	4 EXCEEDS EXPECTATIONS
SCIENCE CONTENT	The presentation lacks information and shows that you do not understand the rock cycle, *or* the presentation shows consistent misconceptions.	The presentation shows correct understanding of the rock cycle but lacks details, *or* demonstrates minor misconceptions.	The presentation includes appropriate and detailed information about the rock cycle that shows an overall understanding.	The presentation has thorough and detailed information about the rock cycle, showing an understanding that is distinguished (very strong).
USE OF SCIENCE VOCABULARY	The presentation does not include enough science vocabulary to show understanding, *or* the presentation uses terms incorrectly.	The presentation includes some relevant science vocabulary, but needs more to adequately show knowledge.	The presentation consistently uses science vocabulary in the appropriate context.	The presentation uses extensive and appropriate science vocabulary throughout.
ORAL PRESENTATION	The presentation is unprepared and unclear.	Parts of the presentation are unclear because of a lack of organization, volume, or eye contact.	The presentation is organized and has consistent eye contact and a clear speaking style. Your teaching comes across well.	The presentation has the "wow" factor, and the teaching method really captures the class's attention!

Use the organizer on page 65 to help plan your presentation of the rock cycle.

Name: _____ Date: _____

Presenting ... the Rock Cycle!

Your assignment is to use creative writing to teach the class about the rock cycle. You can work independently or in a small group (the more minds involved, the higher the expectations). Your goal is to show your understanding in a clear, creative way. Here are some options for how you could teach the class:

*Write a poem. *Write a short story. *Perform a skit (you must provide a script).

*Write a song. *Choose another idea that is *approved* by your teacher.

Vocabulary I could use from this unit in my writing includes the following:

You will be scored according to the following rubric:

AREA	1 DOES NOT MEET EXPECTATIONS	2 PARTIALLY MEETS EXPECTATIONS	3 MEETS EXPECTATIONS	4 EXCEEDS EXPECTATIONS
SCIENCE CONTENT	The presentation lacks information and shows that you do not understand the rock cycle, *or* the presentation shows consistent misconceptions.	The presentation shows correct understanding of the rock cycle but lacks details, *or* demonstrates minor misconceptions.	The presentation includes appropriate and detailed information about the rock cycle that shows an overall understanding.	The presentation has thorough and detailed information about the rock cycle, showing an understanding that is distinguished (very strong).
USE OF SCIENCE VOCABULARY	The presentation does not include enough science vocabulary to show understanding, *or* the presentation uses terms incorrectly.	The presentation includes some relevant science vocabulary, but needs more to adequately show knowledge.	The presentation consistently uses science vocabulary in the appropriate context.	The presentation uses extensive and appropriate science vocabulary throughout.
ORAL PRESENTATION	The presentation is unprepared and unclear.	Parts of the presentation are unclear because of a lack of organization, volume, or eye contact.	The presentation is organized and has consistent eye contact and a clear speaking style. Your teaching comes across well.	The presentation has the "wow" factor, and the teaching method really captures the class's attention!
WRITING FLUENCY	Writing flow and errors in sentence structure make the piece difficult to understand.	Writing flow and errors in sentence structure distract the reader.	The sentence structure is correct, and the flow of writing is smooth to the reader.	The sentence structure, flow, and style of writing are distinguished (very strong).
CONVENTIONS	Spelling, capitalization, and punctuation errors make the piece difficult to understand.	Spelling, capitalization, and punctuation errors distract the reader.	The spelling, capitalization, punctuation, and grammar are mostly *or* all correct.	The spelling, capitalization, punctuation, and grammar are distinguished (very strong).

Use the organizer on page 65 to help plan your presentation of the rock cycle.

Name: _____ Date: _____

Presenting ... the Rock Cycle! Organizer

There are many possible journeys through the rock cycle.

Fill in the events and details for a sequence through the rock cycle.

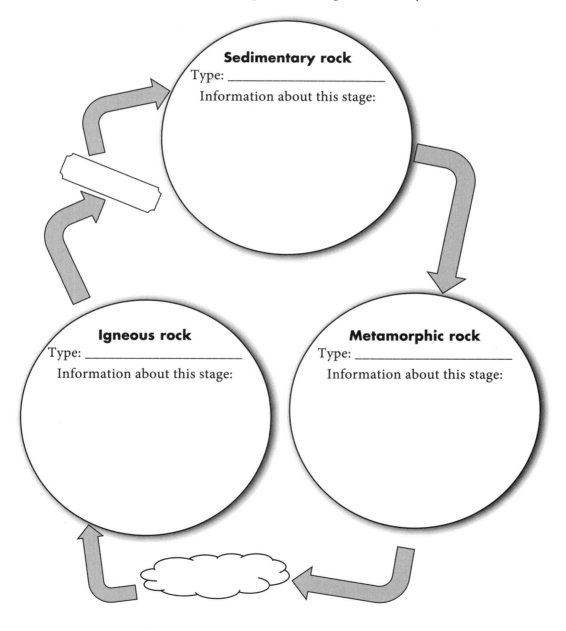

Sedimentary rock
Type: _____
Information about this stage:

Igneous rock
Type: _____
Information about this stage:

Metamorphic rock
Type: _____
Information about this stage:

Presenting ... the Rock Cycle! Model

Mud Is My Mother

Mud is my mother
Earth is my father
The weight of their love
forms me

I grow from
weak specks of sediment
Grinding, grueling
Painful, pressure

Smidgens of silt and soil
merge into one
as I become sedimentary

No longer do I flow through the water
Now I am still

How I long to be metamorphic
Like a colorful butterfly
Changing, evolving
Never stagnant, never stale

How I yearn to be igneous
Flowing freely in fire
Born from ashes

My only hope
is that with time
I will weather
and erode
and return
to the earth
as sediment
And take my journey again
To form a new
me

CHAPTER 11

SCI-FI: WHAT WOULD THE WORLD BE LIKE IF THE KT ASTEROID HAD NEVER HIT?

Writing Styles

Narrative writing, newspaper article

Purpose

Students will work individually to apply knowledge and vocabulary of the mass extinctions caused by the KT asteroid to a piece of science fiction writing.

Overview

The goal of this activity is to use scientific knowledge and critical thinking skills to describe how Earth's organisms and landscape would be different today if the KT asteroid had *never* collided with Earth.

Language Arts Connections

Before discussing the prompts on the organizer, students will benefit from being shown images of what scientists envision Earth to have looked like 66 million years ago. This will help students conceptualize what evolutionary changes may or may not have occurred. Students will then brainstorm about how the setting of Earth would be different today. What would the landscape look like? Would there be dinosaurs? Would humans be here? What species could have evolved?

The model shown, of a newspaper article, also serves as a writing example of a parody. This model is a satire of many ethical issues that currently exist about the quickly expanding human population but applied to the T. rex.

Differentiation Strategies

Students who need more of a challenge can focus on what adaptations cause some species to live and other species to die, emphasizing genetic variation and the emergence of new species.

To prevent misconceptions, you must explain that there is much evidence to show that the KT asteroid hit and mass extinctions occurred. Students should understand that they are writing science fiction. They are imagining what the world would be like today if the asteroid missed Earth 65 million years ago and 75% of Earth's organisms did not become extinct.

Some students may need to write based on actual evidence rather than science fiction to avoid misconception. They could write about the asteroid hitting and their vision of the collision and the aftermath of extinctions that it caused. This option has more concrete thinking, but it still gets at the core of the assignment, which is showing their understanding of the time period, the extinctions that occurred, and the evolutionary opportunities that ensued.

Connections to the *Next Generation Science Standards*

- **3-LS4-2:** Use evidence to construct an explanation for how the variations in characteristics among individuals of the same species may provide advantages in surviving, finding mates, and reproducing.

- **3-LS4-3:** Construct an argument with evidence that in a particular habitat some organisms can survive well, some survive less well, and some cannot survive at all.

- **MS-ESS2-2:** Construct an explanation based on evidence for how geoscience processes have changed Earth's surface at varying time and spatial scales.

- **MS-ESS3-4:** Construct an argument supported by evidence for how increases in human population and per-capita consumption of natural resources impact Earth's systems.

- **MS-LS4-1:** Analyze and interpret data for patterns in the fossil record that document the existence, diversity, extinction, and change of life forms throughout the history of life on Earth under the assumption that natural laws operate today as in the past.

- **MS-LS4-2:** Apply scientific ideas to construct an explanation for the anatomical similarities and differences among modern organisms and between modern and fossil organisms to infer evolutionary relationships.

- **MS-LS4-4:** Construct an explanation based on evidence that describes how genetic variations of traits in a population increase some individuals' probability of surviving and reproducing in a specific environment.

- **HS-ESS1-6:** Apply scientific reasoning and evidence from ancient Earth materials, meteorites, and other planetary surfaces to construct an account of Earth's formation and early history.

- **HS-ESS3-1:** Construct an explanation based on evidence for how the availability of natural resources, occurrence of natural hazards, and changes in climate have influenced human activity.

- **HS-LS2-8:** Evaluate the evidence for the role of group behavior on individual and species' chances to survive and reproduce.

- **HS-LS4-1:** Communicate scientific information that common ancestry and biological evolution are supported by multiple lines of empirical evidence.

- **HS-LS4-2:** Construct an explanation based on evidence that the process of evolution primarily results from four factors: (1) the potential for a species to increase in number, (2) the heritable genetic variation of individuals in a species due to mutation and sexual reproduction, (3) competition for limited resources, (4) the proliferation of those organisms that are better able to survive and reproduce in the environment.

- **HS-LS4-4:** Construct an explanation based on evidence for how natural selection leads to adaptation of populations.

- **HS-LS4-5:** Evaluate the evidence supporting claims that changes in environmental conditions may result in (1) increases in the number of individuals of some species, (2) the emergence of new species over time, (3) the extinction of other species.

Applications to Other Science Areas

Students could write a science fiction piece about some of the ethical aspects in genetics and technology. For example, what if parents could design their child's features and traits? Or what engineering and design features could a car of the future have to meet the needs of our changing world?

Name: _____ Date: _____

Sci-Fi: What Would the World Be Like If the KT Asteroid Had Never Hit?

About 65 million years ago an asteroid collided with Earth near Mexico's Yucatan Peninsula. The asteroid's impact caused atmospheric changes to Earth, which led to the extinction of 75% of Earth's plant and animal species. But *what if* that hadn't happened. How would our planet and the species that live here be different without this mass extinction event? What evolutionary opportunities would ensue? For this assignment, you will write a *science fiction* piece that answers the following question: What would Earth look like today if the KT asteroid had never hit?

There are a variety of writing approaches that you can use to answer this question. Some options for your science fiction piece include a fictional story, a newspaper article, or another idea that is *approved* by your teacher.

You will be scored according to the following rubric:

AREA	1 DOES NOT MEET EXPECTATIONS	2 PARTIALLY MEETS EXPECTATIONS	3 MEETS EXPECTATIONS	4 EXCEEDS EXPECTATIONS
SCIENCE CONTENT	The piece lacks information and shows that you cannot conceptualize how Earth would be different today, *or* the piece shows consistent misconceptions.	The piece shows correct understanding of how Earth could be different today but lacks details, *or* the piece demonstrates misconceptions.	The piece includes appropriate and detailed information that shows an overall understanding of how Earth could be different today.	The piece has thorough and detailed information, with an emphasis on evolutionary opportunities, and shows how Earth could be different today in a way that is distinguished (very strong).
USE OF SCIENCE VOCABULARY	The piece does not include enough science vocabulary to show understanding, *or* uses terms incorrectly.	The piece includes some relevant science vocabulary, but needs more to adequately show knowledge.	The piece consistently uses science vocabulary in the appropriate context.	The piece uses extensive and appropriate science vocabulary throughout.

Use the organizers on pages 72–75 to brainstorm before you begin writing.

Name: _____ Date: _____

Sci-Fi: What Would the World Be Like If the KT Asteroid Had Never Hit?

About 65 million years ago an asteroid collided with Earth near Mexico's Yucatan Peninsula. The asteroid's impact caused atmospheric changes to Earth, which led to the extinction of 75% of Earth's plant and animal species. But *what if* that hadn't happened. How would our planet and the species that live here be different without this mass extinction event? What evolutionary opportunities would ensue? For this assignment, you will write a *science fiction* piece that answers the following question: What would Earth look like today if the KT asteroid had never hit?

There are a variety of writing approaches that you can use to answer this question. Some options for your science fiction piece include a fictional story, a newspaper article, or another idea that is *approved* by your teacher.

You will be scored according to the following rubric:

AREA	1 DOES NOT MEET EXPECTATIONS	2 PARTIALLY MEETS EXPECTATIONS	3 MEETS EXPECTATIONS	4 EXCEEDS EXPECTATIONS
SCIENCE CONTENT	The piece lacks information and shows that you cannot conceptualize how Earth would be different today, *or* the piece shows consistent misconceptions.	The piece shows correct understanding of how Earth could be different today but lacks details, *or* the piece demonstrates misconceptions.	The piece includes appropriate and detailed information that shows an overall understanding of how Earth could be different today.	The piece has thorough and detailed information, with an emphasis on evolutionary opportunities, and shows how Earth could be different today in a way that is distinguished (very strong).
USE OF SCIENCE VOCABULARY	The piece does not include enough science vocabulary to show understanding, *or* the piece uses terms incorrectly.	The piece includes some relevant science vocabulary, but it needs more to adequately show knowledge.	The piece consistently uses science vocabulary in the appropriate context.	The piece uses extensive and appropriate science vocabulary throughout.
WRITING FLUENCY	Writing flow and errors in sentence structure make the piece difficult to understand.	Writing flow and errors in sentence structure distract the reader.	The sentence structure is correct, and the flow of writing is smooth to the reader.	The sentence structure, flow, and style of writing are distinguished (very strong).
CONVENTIONS	Spelling, capitalization, and punctuation errors make the piece difficult to understand.	Spelling, capitalization, and punctuation errors distract the reader.	The spelling, capitalization, punctuation, and grammar are mostly *or* all correct.	The spelling, capitalization, punctuation, and grammar are distinguished (very strong).

Use the organizers on pages 72–75 to brainstorm before you begin writing.

CREATIVE WRITING IN SCIENCE

Name: _____ Date: _____

Sci-Fi: What Would the World Be Like If the KT Asteroid Had Never Hit? Organizer

What are some of the most significant extinctions that occurred because of the KT asteroid?
Without those extinctions, what species do you think would dominate the Earth today?
Would those species look the same? Or would they have evolved? Explain.

Would humans be here today? Explain.

If so, how would humans be different? If not, would there be any civilizations?

What would Earth's landscape look like today?

Name: _____ Date: _____

Sci-Fi: What Would the World Be Like If the KT Asteroid Had Never Hit? Narrative Writing Organizer

From whose perspective will the story be told? _____

Where does the story take place? _____

Describe the setting: _____

_____

What is the main conflict in the story? _____

_____

How does the conflict get resolved? _____

_____

What is a possible first sentence that will pull the reader in?

_____

_____

Fill in the chart below with the sequence of events that could happen in your story:

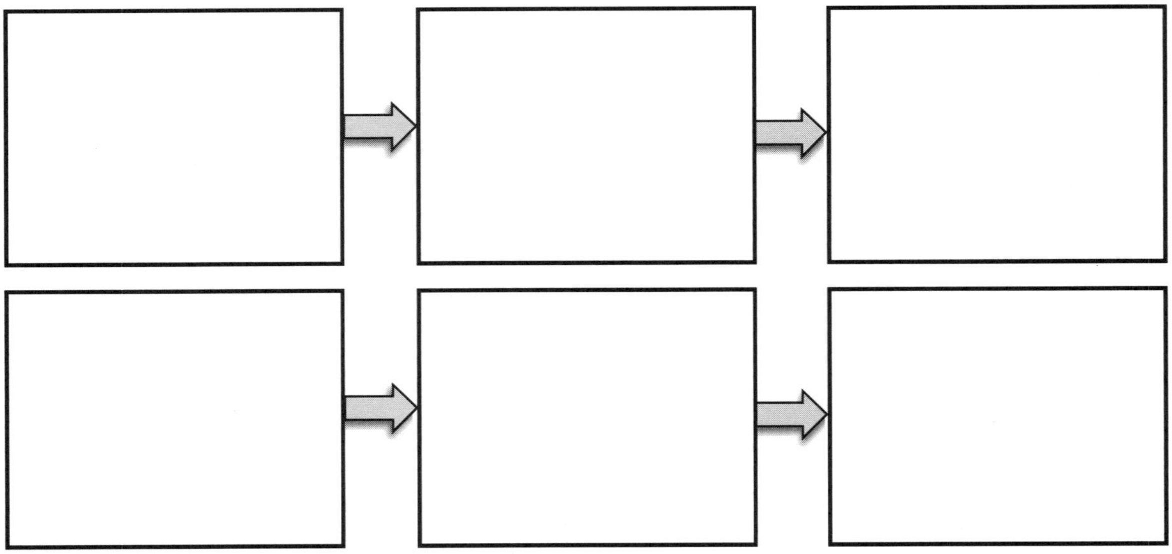

How will the story end?_____

_____

Name: _____ Date: _____

Sci-Fi: What Would the World Be Like If the KT Asteroid Had Never Hit? Newspaper Article Organizer

Newspaper articles are based on events that occurred. What event would be worthy of a front-page story? Answer the *who, what, where, when, why,* and *how* to describe the event that this article is about. Use this information when you write the article.

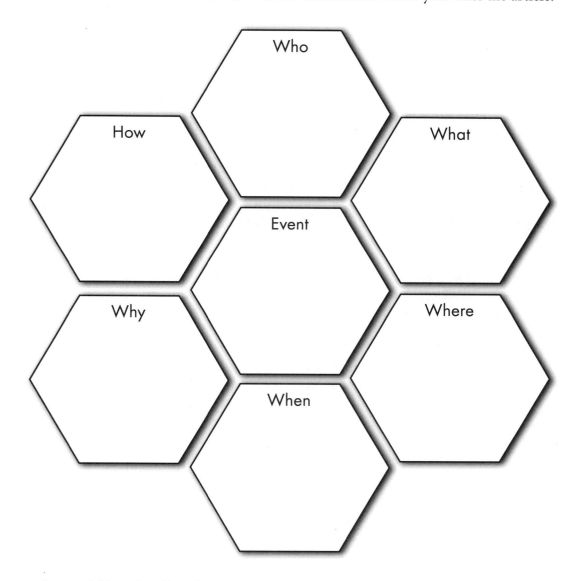

What could be a headline for your story? _____

_____

Sci-Fi: What Would the World Be Like If the KT Asteroid Had Never Hit? Newspaper Article Model

THE T. REX TIMES

Population Hits Record High!
By Tyrann O. Saurus

It's official: There are more Tyrannosauruses alive today than ever before. According to the results of the most recent census, this pattern could lead to a doubling of our population over the next 30 years. The majority of Tyrannosauruses alive today range from juvenile to middle aged. Less than 10% of all Tyrannosauruses are considered to be seniors; the main reason for seniors dying is competition. With so many Tyrannosauruses, the fastest and most aggressive animals get the prey. Some say this is good because it helps control the population. Others say this is cruel. Tyrannosauruses need to support one another, especially our aging population. This leads to the age-old question: What is best for our species? Survival of the strongest or survival of all? Is it best for a T. rex to eat a Triceratops all by himself? Or should he eat less and share his kill with others? Does he even know how to share? Or is the very evolution of our species tied to individual success and survival? These are questions that are arising among T. rex communities around the world. With so many Tyrannosauruses alive that are able to reproduce, what will the world look like as the Tyrannosaurus population continues to increase? Will there be enough food for all? Many T. rexes have already noticed that, because of the increased number of predators, finding quality prey has become harder. With less food, how will Tyrannosauruses treat each other? The Tyrannosaurus is not the first species in this predicament, and it certainly will not be the last. However, decisions need to be made to help preserve our species and the quality of life that many Tyrannosauruses have become accustomed to.

Sci-Fi: What Would the World Be Like If the KT Asteroid Had Never Hit? Narrative Story Model

Current Day: The Age of the Nets

First we tried stone walls; then logs stacked 5 meters high. They were useless. They tore through them as easily as they do flesh. For years our people lived in trees, which offered some protection. Brave souls would forage the forests searching for food, while lookouts in the trees would whistle when a dinosaur came near. Luckily, dinosaurs are loud as they stomp through the forest. As long as they don't see you, you're OK, but if they do see you, it's already too late. Despite evolving to be smaller over time and faster, their vision is still not good. But, if they do see you, it means they are less than 20 meters away. Even the fastest person can't get up a tree by the time they get to you. Our speed, strength, and survival skills are nothing compared with theirs. They stand high above us with their scaly skin and sharp claws ready to attack. We thought we would live in fear forever, but over time we learned that our biggest threat to the dinosaurs is, in fact, our intelligence.

The story goes that it all began with the hopes of a better, more comfortable night's sleep. Someone collected vines and wove them together into a sleeping hammock that they hung from the branches of a tree. Everyone became jealous and instantly wanted their own hammock. From the hammocks came more purposes for the nets we wove. We trapped birds and small prey and ate them. With the nets, we shifted from being herbivores to being omnivores. Once you taste meat, you daydream about what larger prey would taste like.

Legend says that was how the idea came to catch a small dinosaur and eat it. There would be plenty of meat to share, and we could make weapons out of its teeth and claws. The problem is, where there is a small dinosaur, there could be others nearby. With great planning and waiting, the opportunity finally came; however, one opportunity can often lead to another. The net did not catch the dinosaur as the hunters thought it would. Instead, the net got caught in a tree. Even small dinosaurs attack humans, so when the dinosaur saw people, he instantly charged ready to pounce with his sharp teeth and claws. But something happened that day. The net was hanging from the tree to the ground, and when the dinosaur got close to the net, he stopped and turned around. It was the first time that anyone had survived a dinosaur attack. Word spread quickly and an idea came to my people. What if all dinosaurs feared nets? What if instinct told them to turn back?

All the people in our community came together and crafted enormous nets to hang from the trees. We created a wall of nets around us and our hopes came true. The dinosaurs did not attack. A net was, in fact, for us stronger than a stone wall. With the nets up, more human babies are being born and life is getting easier and easier for us. We now have the Earth at our fingertips. We live in permanent shelters and have begun planting seeds to grow our own food. With time, we plan to put up enough nets to banish dinosaurs entirely from our land. The opportunities are endless now that we know how powerful the human mind can be.

CHAPTER 12

PACKING LIST FOR THE PLANETS

Writing Style

Expository

Purpose

Students will work individually to apply knowledge and vocabulary of a planet to a piece of creative writing.

Overview

For this activity, students create a list of supplies that they would need to visit a planet in our solar system. In the process, students will show their understanding of the planet. With each item, students should include a description of why it is necessary.

Language Arts Connections

The primary purpose of this task is to show knowledge of a planet through informative writing. However, there is also a fantasy aspect to this assignment. As a result, a humorous tone could be fitting for this piece of writing.

Because students will need to research information about a planet, it may benefit them to learn about the appropriate ways to conduct research and the most reliable forums for gathering information. It may also help students to see how to correctly cite sources.

Differentiation Strategies

Some students may struggle with the openness of the assignment and may benefit from requirements being more specific. For example, students could choose the five most important items to bring and explain why they are necessary. An alternative assignment could be to make a travel brochure about a planet. This brochure would include similar information and facts, but it would be written more descriptively.

To avoid student misconceptions, emphasize the fantasy aspect of this assignment. Many of these planets are so far away that it could take years to travel to them. For example, Neptune is more than four billion kilometers (29 AU) away, and it would take about 12 years to travel there by spacecraft. Researching this information could improve students' realization of the challenges that come with humans traveling far distances in space. Students could research how much food they would need, what they would do with their trash, and how they would exercise to keep their muscles in shape over such a long journey.

Connections to the *Next Generation Science Standards*

- **MS-ESS1-2:** Develop and use a model to describe the role of gravity in the motions within galaxies and the solar systems.
- **MS-ESS1-3:** Analyze and interpret data to determine scale properties of objects in the solar system.

Applications to Other Science Areas

Students could make a packing list or a travel brochure for visiting a biome, the layers of the Earth, or a period in Earth's history.

Name: _____ Date: _____

Packing List for the Planets

To show your understanding of one of our solar system's planets, create a packing list of the essential items someone would need to survive if he or she were to visit that planet. For each item, explain how it will help ensure survival using specific information about the planet. For example, if someone traveled to Mercury, he or she would need a space suit that could withstand temperatures ranging from −170°C at night to 430°C during the day.

Planet I will be researching: _____

> **Vocabulary I could use from this unit in my writing includes the following:**
>
>
>
>
>
>
>

You will be scored according to the following rubric:

AREA	1 DOES NOT MEET EXPECTATIONS	2 PARTIALLY MEETS EXPECTATIONS	3 MEETS EXPECTATIONS	4 EXCEEDS EXPECTATIONS
SCIENCE CONTENT	The list lacks information and shows that you do not understand the environment of the planet, *or* the list shows consistent misconceptions.	The list shows correct understanding but lacks details about the planet, *or* the list demonstrates some minor misconceptions.	The list includes appropriate and detailed information about the planet that shows an overall understanding.	The list has thorough and detailed information about the planet, showing an understanding that is distinguished (very strong).
USE OF SCIENCE VOCABULARY	The list does not include enough science vocabulary to show understanding, *or* the list uses terms incorrectly.	The list includes some relevant science vocabulary, but it needs more to adequately show knowledge.	The list consistently uses science vocabulary in the appropriate context.	The list uses extensive and appropriate science vocabulary throughout.

Use the organizer on page 83 to plan your writing piece.

Name: _____ Date: _____

Packing List for the Planets

To show your understanding of one of our solar system's planets, create a packing list of the essential items someone would need to survive if he or she were to visit that planet. For each item, explain how it will help ensure survival using specific information about the planet. For example, if someone traveled to Mercury, he or she would need a space suit that could withstand temperatures ranging from −170°C at night to 430°C during the day.

Planet I will be researching:_____

Vocabulary I could use from this unit in my writing includes the following:

You will be scored according to the following rubric:

AREA	1 DOES NOT MEET EXPECTATIONS	2 PARTIALLY MEETS EXPECTATIONS	3 MEETS EXPECTATIONS	4 EXCEEDS EXPECTATIONS
SCIENCE CONTENT	The list lacks information and shows that you do not understand the environment of the planet, or the list shows consistent misconceptions.	The list shows correct understanding but lacks details about the planet, or list demonstrates some minor misconceptions.	The list includes appropriate and detailed information about the planet that shows an overall understanding.	The list has thorough and detailed information about the planet, showing an understanding that is distinguished (very strong).
USE OF SCIENCE VOCABULARY	The list does not include enough vocabulary to show understanding, or the list uses terms incorrectly.	The list includes some relevant science vocabulary, but it needs more to adequately show knowledge.	The list consistently uses science vocabulary in the appropriate context.	The list uses extensive and appropriate science vocabulary throughout.
WRITING FLUENCY	Writing flow and errors in sentence structure make the list difficult to understand.	Writing flow and errors in sentence structure distract the reader.	The sentence structure is correct, and the flow of writing is smooth to the reader.	The sentence structure, flow, and style of writing are distinguished (very strong).
CONVENTIONS	Spelling, capitalization, and punctuation errors make the list difficult to understand.	Spelling, capitalization, and punctuation errors distract the reader.	The spelling, capitalization, punctuation, and grammar are mostly or all correct.	The spelling, capitalization, punctuation, and grammar are distinguished (very strong).

Use the organizer on page 83 to plan your writing piece.

Name: _____ Date: _____

Packing List for the Planets: Organizer

As you research the planet, keep track of facts you learn and how they could lead to items for your packing list.

FACT ABOUT THE PLANET	ITEM(S) NEEDED FOR PACKING LIST

Packing List for the Planets: Model for Mercury

To help prepare you for your trip to Mercury, be sure to pack the following items:

- **Space suit with temperature control:** Mercury has a large range in temperature during the day and night. The suit must withstand temperatures from –170°C at night to 430°C during the day.

- **Oxygen:** Because Mercury has little to no atmosphere, you must bring your own oxygen. There are also no plants to create oxygen.

- **Food and water:** If you are staying for a full year on Mercury, which is 88 (Earth) days, you will need to bring a lot of food and water. You will also need food and water for the long trip there and back.

- **Solar panels:** Because Mercury is the closest planet to the Sun, you will want solar panels to harvest the Sun's energy.

- **Meteor detector:** Because Mercury lacks atmosphere, you have little protection from meteors. The detector will let you know when meteors are coming; otherwise, there is little chance of survival if you are hit by a meteor. You will see craters all over Mercury, which were caused by meteors.

- **Rover:** The diameter of Mercury is almost 4,900 kilometers. To really travel this planet, you will need a vehicle (preferably one with heat and air conditioning).

- **Strong ultraviolet sunglasses:** The Sun will look three times bigger on Mercury than it looks on Earth. This intense sunlight can irreversibly damage your eyes.

- **Sleeping mask:** Because Mercury rotates so slowly, one day on Mercury takes the equivalent of about 59 Earth days. You will be in the sunlight for a long time, so be sure to have a mask so you can get a break from the bright sun and take a nap.

- **Lots of books, movies, and music:** The journey to Mercury is about 77,000,000 kilometers, so it will be important to have entertainment for the ride!

With these items, you will be sure to have a safe, fun, and educational trip.

Enjoy your journey!

CHAPTER 13

LETTER FROM THE MOON TO EARTH

Writing Styles

Persuasive, argumentative, letter

Purpose

Students will work individually to apply knowledge and vocabulary about the Moon to a piece of fictional writing.

Overview

For this activity students write a letter from the Moon to Earth explaining why the Moon is important. Students will show their understanding of the Moon and the effect that the Moon has on Earth, with an emphasis on showing their understanding of gravity.

Language Arts Connections

Discuss the proper letter-writing format, which is demonstrated in the graphic organizer.

This assignment is an example of personification. Students are giving human qualities and emotions to the Moon, which is not a human being. Therefore, it will be helpful for students to think about what tone they would like the letter to have. Perhaps the Moon is like a younger sibling trying to get attention from Earth, or maybe the Moon is a sensible, old soul.

Differentiation Strategies

A more challenging assignment could be for the Moon to have a diary, perhaps organized by its lunar phases. The diary entries could include how the Moon felt when it broke off from Earth. Maybe the Moon is lonely. Maybe it is jealous of Earth's atmosphere and organisms. Maybe its craters feel like battle scars. Maybe it loves watching Earth's tides. The diary would have more emotions than a letter because the Moon does not have an audience but is writing simply to express its own feelings.

To avoid student misconceptions, you should emphasize that personification is a literary device and that the Moon does not actually have these emotions. Personification is a writing tool that enhances creativity and helps engage the reader.

Connections to the *Next Generation Science Standards*

- **5-PS2-1:** Support an argument that the gravitational force exerted by Earth on objects is directed down.

- **MS-ESS1-1:** Develop and use a model of the Earth-Sun-Moon system to describe the cyclic patterns of lunar phases, eclipses of the Sun and Moon, and seasons.

- **MS-ESS1-2:** Develop and use a model to describe the role of gravity in the motions within galaxies and the solar system.

- **MS-ESS1-3:** Analyze and interpret data to determine scale properties of objects in the solar system.

- **MS-ESS2-4:** Develop a model to describe the cycling of water through Earth's systems driven by energy from the Sun and the force of gravity.

- **HS-ESS1-6:** Apply scientific reasoning and evidence from ancient Earth materials, meteorites, and other planetary surfaces to construct an account of Earth's formation and early history.

Applications to Other Science Areas

You could have students write a letter or thank-you note from a plant to the Sun, from humans to an element, or from one organism to another in a symbiotic relationship.

Name: _____ Date: _____

Letter From the Moon to Earth

To show your understanding of the Moon, write a letter from the Moon's perspective to Earth. Think about what it is like to be the Moon and what the Moon would say to Earth, when given the chance. What importance does the Moon have to Earth? What personality would the Moon have? Is it confident? Lonely? Wise? Give the Moon strong voice and personality.

What type of personality would the Moon have? _____

> Knowledge or vocabulary I could use from this unit in my writing includes the following:
>
>
>
>
>
>

You will be scored according to the following rubric:

AREA	1 DOES NOT MEET EXPECTATIONS	2 PARTIALLY MEETS EXPECTATIONS	3 MEETS EXPECTATIONS	4 EXCEEDS EXPECTATIONS
SCIENCE CONTENT	The letter lacks information and shows that you do not understand the Moon in relation to Earth, *or* the letter shows consistent misconceptions.	The letter shows correct understanding but lacks details about the Moon's importance, *or* the letter demonstrates some minor misconceptions.	The letter includes appropriate and detailed information about the Moon's importance that shows an overall understanding.	The letter has thorough and detailed information about the Moon's importance, showing an understanding that is distinguished (very strong).
USE OF SCIENCE VOCABULARY	The letter does not include enough science vocabulary to show understanding, *or* the letter uses terms incorrectly.	The letter includes some relevant science vocabulary, but it needs more to adequately show knowledge.	The letter consistently uses science vocabulary in the appropriate context.	The letter uses extensive and appropriate science vocabulary throughout.

Use the letter organizer on page 89 before you begin your final piece.

Name: _____ Date: _____

Letter From the Moon to Earth

To show your understanding of the Moon, write a letter from the Moon's perspective to Earth. Think about what it is like to be the Moon and what the Moon would say to Earth, when given the chance. What importance does the Moon have to Earth? What personality would the Moon have? Is it confident? Lonely? Wise? Give the Moon strong voice and personality.

What type of personality would the Moon have?_____

Knowledge or vocabulary I could use from this unit in my writing includes the following:

You will be scored according to the following rubric:

AREA	1 DOES NOT MEET EXPECTATIONS	2 PARTIALLY MEETS EXPECTATIONS	3 MEETS EXPECTATIONS	4 EXCEEDS EXPECTATIONS
SCIENCE CONTENT	The letter lacks information and shows that you do not understand the Moon in relation to Earth, or the letter shows consistent misconceptions.	The letter shows correct understanding but lacks details about the Moon's importance, or the letter demonstrates some minor misconceptions.	The letter includes appropriate and detailed information about the Moon's importance that shows an overall understanding.	The letter has thorough and detailed information about the Moon's importance, showing an understanding that is distinguished (very strong).
USE OF SCIENCE VOCABULARY	The letter does not include enough vocabulary to show understanding, or the letter uses terms incorrectly.	The letter includes some relevant vocabulary, but it needs more to adequately show knowledge.	The letter consistently uses science vocabulary in the appropriate context.	The letter uses extensive and appropriate science vocabulary throughout.
WRITING FLUENCY	Writing flow and errors in sentence structure make the letter difficult to understand.	Writing flow and errors in sentence structure distract the reader.	The sentence structure is correct, and the flow of writing is smooth to the reader.	The sentence structure, flow, and style of writing are distinguished (very strong).
CONVENTIONS	Spelling, capitalization, and punctuation errors make the letter difficult to understand.	Spelling, capitalization, and punctuation errors distract the reader.	The spelling, capitalization, punctuation, and grammar are mostly or all correct.	The spelling, capitalization, punctuation, and grammar are distinguished (very strong).

Use the letter organizer on page 89 before you begin your final piece.

Letter From the Moon to Earth: Organizer

Sender's address:

Today's date:

Recipient's name and address:

Salutation,

Body of letter (one to three paragraphs):
Facts about the Moon and why it is important:

Salutation,

Signature:

Letter From the Moon to Earth: Model

The Moon
384,400 km
From Earth

April 1, _____

The Earth
3rd planet
From the Sun
Our solar system
Milky Way

Dear Earth,

I write you this letter as a reminder that I am here. I exist. I matter. For more than *four billion years*, you have looked at me as merely a *satellite* orbiting around you. I am grateful that I am connected to you through *gravity*, but I wish that you also felt a connection to me.

Even though I am more than *300,000 km* away from you, I affect you every single day. In ancient times, I helped people keep track of days. The pattern of my phases is predictable and reliable, just like me. The light I give off at night, guides animals to their homes; I guide them to safety. Some of the meteors that hit me, covering me in craters, could have hit you. I am there for you.

However, the most important effect I have on you is the *tides* I create through your *centripetal force* and my own. I know the *Sun* plays a small part in tides, too, but it's mostly me. Without my tides, many species on your planet would not exist. You are lucky enough to have organisms living in your air, land, and sea. I do not, but I get comfort in knowing that my *gravitational pull* on your oceans creates a home for so many. I see the seas *bulge* from my pull, and I feel pride in the influence I have. Please, Earth, just take the time to see all that I do for you. A little *thank you* would go a long way.

Your devoted *satellite*,

Luna
(The Moon)

ENGINEERING AND PHYSICAL SCIENCE ACTIVITIES

CHAPTER 14

INTERVIEW WITH AN ATOM

Writing Styles

Skit, play, interview

Purpose

Students will work with a partner to apply knowledge of elements, atoms, molecules, and bonds (covalent or ionic) to a skit.

Overview

For this activity, a pair of students researches two elements (that can form a bond) and acts out a skit in which they personify two atoms meeting for the first time. Because the elements are meeting, they will ask questions to learn about the properties of the element.

Language Arts Connections

Students should approach the interview with a focus on the who, what, where, when, why, and how for information about the element. For example, who discovered the element? What is its classification? What is its atomic mass? Where is it found? And how many electrons, protons, and neutrons does it have?

Students may need a model of how to write in a play format. They should have the character's name and then a colon followed by the character's speaking line. If there are stage directions, students can write them in italics and parentheses.

The setting of the skit can establish the tone for the play. Is this simply a question-and-answer interview, or does the interview occur in an actual setting as in the model provided? The model takes place at a location for speed dating, which creates a natural atmosphere for the interviews and the types of questions that are asked.

Because students will need to research information about an element, it may benefit them to learn about the appropriate ways to conduct research and the most reliable forums for gathering information. It may also help students to see how to correctly cite sources.

Differentiation Strategies

To help with differentiation, tell students which elements can form a bond. For example, students may have prior knowledge that elements such as hydrogen and oxygen can form a bond, but they may not know that other elements such as potassium and chlorine can bond too. In addition, you may want to tell students what vocabulary from the unit they need to incorporate into their skit.

Connections to the *Next Generation Science Standards*

- **MS-PS1-1:** Develop models to describe the atomic composition of simple molecules and extended structures.

- **MS-PS1-5:** Develop and use a model to describe how the total number of atoms does not change in a chemical reaction and thus mass is conserved.

- **HS-PS1-1:** Use the periodic table as a model to predict the relative properties of elements based on the patterns of electrons in the outermost energy level of atoms.

- **HS-PS1-2:** Construct and revise an explanation for the outcome of a simple chemical reaction based on the outermost electron states of atoms, trends in the periodic table, and knowledge of the patterns of chemical properties.

- **HS-PS1-8:** Develop models to illustrate the changes in the composition of the nucleus of the atom and the energy released during the processes of fission, fusion, and radioactive decay.

Applications to Other Science Areas

You could have students conduct an interview between two organisms in a symbiotic relationship, two weather events, or two famous inventors.

Name: _____ Date: _____

Interview With an Atom

To show your understanding of atoms, research an element, then work collaboratively with another student (who researched a different element) to write a skit about what happens when your atoms make a covalent or ionic bond and form a molecule. Use the skit as an opportunity to show your knowledge of elements, atoms, molecules, and bonds. Your script must be handed in at the time of your presentation.

The element I will research:_____ The symbol for this element:_____ Four elements that an atom of this element could bond with:_____

Knowledge or vocabulary I could use from this unit in my writing includes the following:

You will be scored on the following rubric:

AREA	1 DOES NOT MEET EXPECTATIONS	2 PARTIALLY MEETS EXPECTATIONS	3 MEETS EXPECTATIONS	4 EXCEEDS EXPECTATIONS
SCIENCE CONTENT	The skit lacks information and shows that you do not understand the concepts of elements, *or* the skit shows consistent misconceptions.	The skit shows correct understanding but lacks details, *or* the skit demonstrates some minor misconceptions.	The skit includes appropriate and detailed information about elements that shows an overall understanding.	The skit has thorough and detailed information about elements, showing an understanding that is distinguished (very strong).
ORAL PRESENTATION	The skit is unprepared and unclear.	Parts of the skit are unclear because of a lack of organization, volume, or eye contact.	The skit is organized and has consistent eye contact and a clear speaking style.	The skit has the "wow" factor and really captures the class's attention!

Use the organizer on page 97 before you begin writing your script.

Name: _____ Date: _____

Interview With an Atom

To show your understanding of atoms, research an element, then work collaboratively with another student (who researched a different element) to write a skit about what happens when your atoms make a covalent or ionic bond and form a molecule. Use the skit as an opportunity to show your knowledge of elements, atoms, molecules, and bonds. Your script must be handed in at the time of your presentation.

The element I will research:_____ The symbol for this element:_____ Four elements that an atom of this element could bond with:_____

Knowledge or vocabulary I could use from this unit in my writing includes the following:

You will be scored on the following rubric:

AREA	1 DOES NOT MEET EXPECTATIONS	2 PARTIALLY MEETS EXPECTATIONS	3 MEETS EXPECTATIONS	4 EXCEEDS EXPECTATIONS
SCIENCE CONTENT	The skit lacks information and shows that you do not understand the concepts of elements, or the skit shows consistent misconceptions.	The skit shows correct understanding but lacks details, or the skit demonstrates some minor misconceptions.	The skit includes appropriate and detailed information about elements that shows an overall understanding.	The skit has thorough and detailed information about elements and shows an understanding that is distinguished (very strong).
ORAL PRESENTATION	The skit is unprepared and unclear.	Parts of the skit are unclear because of a lack of organization, volume, or eye contact.	The skit is organized and has consistent eye contact and a clear speaking style.	The skit has the "wow" factor and really captures the class's attention!
WRITING FLUENCY	Writing flow and errors in sentence structure make the skit difficult to understand.	Writing flow and errors in sentence structure distract the reader.	The sentence structure is correct, and the flow of writing is smooth to the reader.	The sentence structure, flow, and style of writing are distinguished (very strong).
CONVENTIONS	Spelling, capitalization, and punctuation errors make the skit difficult to understand.	Spelling, capitalization, and punctuation errors distract the reader.	The spelling, capitalization, punctuation, and grammar are mostly or all correct.	The spelling, capitalization, punctuation, and grammar are distinguished (very strong).

Use the organizer on page 97 before you begin writing your script.

Name: _____ Date: _____

Interview With an Atom: Organizer

Answer the *who, what, where, when, why*, and *how* questions with information about your element.

When your background information is complete, collaborate with a partner to write a script that teaches the audience about the two elements and tells the story of how they form a bond. Be sure to use vocabulary from this unit in your skit.

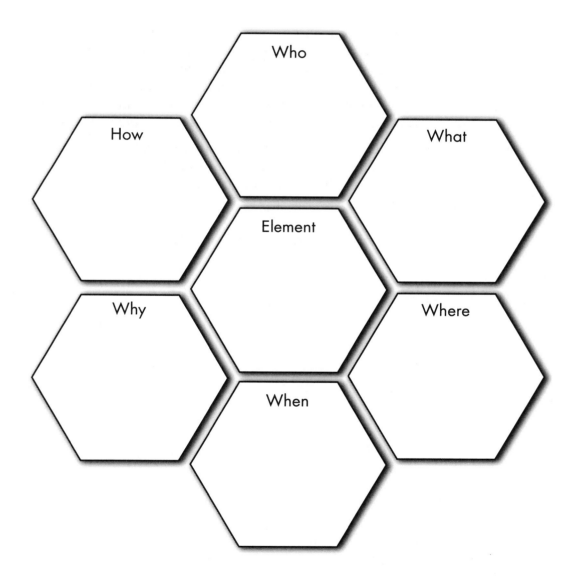

Interview With an Atom: Model for Salt (NaCl)

Salt: A Love Story

(*The scene begins with a sodium and a chlorine atom on opposite sides of the room, each wearing a label that says their name and information about the element. A sign on the door says "Element Speed Dating: Tonight from 8 p.m. to 9 p.m."*)

Sodium: (*talking to self*) I know that I can exist on my own, but something about me feels *unstable*. It's like I'm missing something or … someone. I doubt that I'll find anyone willing to give me more *electrons*. Maybe, but I doubt it. I have to approach tonight as someone who is ready to give. One electron really isn't that much to give away. I have to remember that by being able to give, I will also receive the *stability* I need.

Chlorine: (*talking to self*) I need to come across as confident and likeable. I am so close to being complete. I only need one more electron in my *valence shell*. Just one more. There has to be someone out there with just one electron to give.

(*Sodium and Chlorine wander around the room, then they are pulled toward each other.*)

Chlorine: Hi, what's your name?

Sodium: I'm Sodium.

Chlorine: (*tries to be confident, but is clearly nervous*) So where are you from?

Sodium: (*sounds insecure*) Everywhere, really. I'm one of the more common elements.

Chlorine: Are you a …

Sodium: I'm an *alkali metal*.

Chlorine: Oh, so you're pretty *reactive*?

Sodium: Yes, I am, but please don't judge me on that.

Chlorine: It's OK. Some of my closest friends are alkali metals.

Sodium: Oh, good. I was afraid you'd leave when you found out, and then I'd never even know your name.

Chlorine: My name's Chlorine.

Sodium: That's a beautiful name.

Chlorine: (*embarrassed*) Thank you, Sodium. Let me tell you about me. My *atomic number* is 17. My *atomic mass* is around 35 amu. I'm a *halogen*. I've obviously been around for a long time, but I was first produced in 1774 by Carl Wilhelm Scheele. (*notices Sodium look around the room*) Um, I have seven electrons in my *outermost shell*.

Sodium: (*excited*) Really! I was just looking around the room amazed that someone like you is even talking to me. You won't believe this, but I actually came here tonight hoping to meet someone who needed just one more electron in their outermost shell.

Chlorine: By any chance do you have one electron to give?

Sodium: I do. I knew I felt an *attraction* to you, but please know that it's more than just your electrons. Did I mention that *green* is my favorite color? I can't help but notice your green sheen.

Chlorine: (*self-conscious*) Oh, I didn't think you'd notice. *Silver* looks really nice on you. (*looks around the room*) I told myself I would take my time and find the right *element*, but I'm really attracted to you too.

Sodium: I know you've got a lot of options, and I'm just boring sodium, but I think there might be something really special here.

Chlorine: *Ionic bonds* are my favorite kind of *bond*.

Sodium: I know it may not last forever, but we're both so close to being stable. You have one too few and I have one too many. It almost feels like …

Chlorine: Fate.

Sodium: You know we'd make *NaCl*. *Salt* is one of the most important minerals.

Chlorine: It's always been one of my favorites. *Salt* is not only a mineral but also edible. It's put on roads to keep people safe in the winter, and at one point it was even used as a form of money. People can't live without it. It helps regulate the … heartbeat.

Sodium: It certainly does (*reaches for Chlorine's hand*).

(*Sodium and Chlorine hold hands and walk out the door together.*)

CHAPTER 15

INSTRUCTIONAL MANUAL: HOW TO FLY

Writing Style

Expository

Purpose

Students will work individually to apply knowledge and vocabulary about the physics of flight.

Overview

For this activity, students write a step-by-step instructional manual for anything that flies, such as a plane, kite, bird, or glider. By writing this in steps, students will be able to identify and analyze the sequence of events that leads to flight and demonstrate their scientific vocabulary.

Language Arts Connections

This form of expository writing is organized as a how-to guide, which is structured through a series of steps. Sequence writing has many transitional words that would be beneficial for students to learn. Some transitional words are *next, for example, therefore, as a result, however,* and *finally*. Although the manual is not structured in paragraphs, the first step should sound like an introduction, whereas the final step should read as a conclusion.

Because students will need to research information about something that flies, it may benefit them to learn about the appropriate ways to conduct research and the most reliable forums for gathering information. It may also help students to see how to correctly cite sources.

Differentiation Strategies

It would be helpful to give some students a list of key vocabulary from the unit to incorporate in their writing. In addition, the physics of flight is more complex for some objects or animals, so that could differentiate the assignment.

Students could also focus on the optimal design aspect of this assignment by researching various engineering and design models. An additional challenge could be for students to create their own design for which they describe the steps of flight.

Connections to the *Next Generation Science Standards*

- **3-ETS1-1:** Define a simple design problem reflecting a need or a want that includes specified criteria for success and constraints on materials, time, or cost.

- **3-ETS1-2:** Generate and compare multiple possible solutions to a problem based on how well each is likely to meet the criteria and constraints of the problem.

- **MS-ETS1-2:** Evaluate competing design solutions using a systematic process to determine how well they meet the criteria and constraints of a problem.

- **MS-ETS1-3:** Analyze data from tests to determine similarities and differences among several design solutions to identify the best characteristics of each that can be combined into a new solution to best meet the criteria for success.

- **MS-ETS1-4:** Develop a model to generate data for iterative testing and modification of a proposed object, tool, or process such that an optimal design can be achieved.

- **HS-ETS1-2:** Design a solution to a complex real-word problem by breaking it down into smaller, more manageable problems that can be solved through engineering.

Applications to Other Science Areas

You could have students write an instructional manual or how-to guide for the process of mitosis or meiosis, the way electricity works, or the way tectonic plates move.

Name: _____ Date: _____

Instructional Manual: How to Fly

You will demonstrate what you have learned about the physics of flight by writing an instructional manual that shows the steps for how to fly. You can write this manual for any object or organism that flies, such as a plane, kite, bird, or glider. Be sure to incorporate vocabulary from this unit.

What will you write this instructional manual for?_____

Knowledge or vocabulary I could use from this unit in my writing includes the following:

You will be scored according to the following rubric:

AREA	1 DOES NOT MEET EXPECTATIONS	2 PARTIALLY MEETS EXPECTATIONS	3 MEETS EXPECTATIONS	4 EXCEEDS EXPECTATIONS
SCIENCE CONTENT	The manual lacks information and shows that you do not understand the physics of flight, *or* manual shows consistent misconceptions.	The manual shows correct understanding about the physics of flight but lacks details, *or* the manual demonstrates some minor misconceptions.	The manual includes appropriate and detailed information that shows an overall understanding of the physics of flight.	The manual has thorough and detailed information, showing an understanding of the physics of flight that is distinguished (very strong).
USE OF SCIENCE VOCABULARY	The manual does not include enough science vocabulary to show understanding, *or* the manual uses terms incorrectly.	The manual includes some relevant science vocabulary, but it needs more to adequately show knowledge.	The manual consistently uses science vocabulary in the appropriate context.	The manual uses extensive and appropriate science vocabulary throughout.

Use the organizer on page 105 before you begin your writing.

Name: _____ Date: _____

Instructional Manual: How to Fly

You will demonstrate what you have learned about the physics of flight by writing an instructional manual that shows the steps for how to fly. You can write this manual for any object or organism that flies, such as a plane, kite, bird, or glider. Be sure to incorporate vocabulary from this unit.

What will you write this instructional manual for? _____

Knowledge or vocabulary I could use from this unit in my writing includes the following:

You will be scored according to the following rubric:

AREA	1 DOES NOT MEET EXPECTATIONS	2 PARTIALLY MEETS EXPECTATIONS	3 MEETS EXPECTATIONS	4 EXCEEDS EXPECTATIONS
SCIENCE CONTENT	The manual lacks information and shows that you do not understand the physics of flight, or the manual shows consistent misconceptions.	The manual shows correct understanding about the physics of flight but lacks details, or the manual demonstrates some minor misconceptions.	The manual includes appropriate and detailed information that shows an overall understanding of the physics of flight.	Manual has thorough and detailed information, showing an understanding of the physics of flight that is distinguished (very strong).
USE OF SCIENCE VOCABULARY	The manual does not include enough vocabulary to show understanding, or manual uses terms incorrectly.	The manual includes some relevant vocabulary, but it needs more to adequately show knowledge.	The manual consistently uses science vocabulary in the appropriate context.	Manual uses extensive and appropriate science vocabulary throughout.
WRITING FLUENCY	Writing flow and errors in sentence structure make the manual difficult to understand.	Writing flow and errors in sentence structure distract the reader.	The sentence structure is correct, and the flow of writing is smooth to the reader.	The sentence structure, flow, and style of writing are distinguished (very strong).
CONVENTIONS	Spelling, capitalization, and punctuation errors make the manual difficult to understand.	Spelling, capitalization, and punctuation errors distract the reader.	Spelling, capitalization, punctuation, and grammar are mostly or all correct.	The spelling, capitalization, punctuation, and grammar are distinguished (very strong).

Use the organizer on page 105 before you begin your writing.

Name: _____ Date: _____

Instructional Manual: How to Fly: Organizer

Sequence the events of flight below (you may not need all of the spaces, or you may need more). Add appropriate vocabulary and understanding for each step.

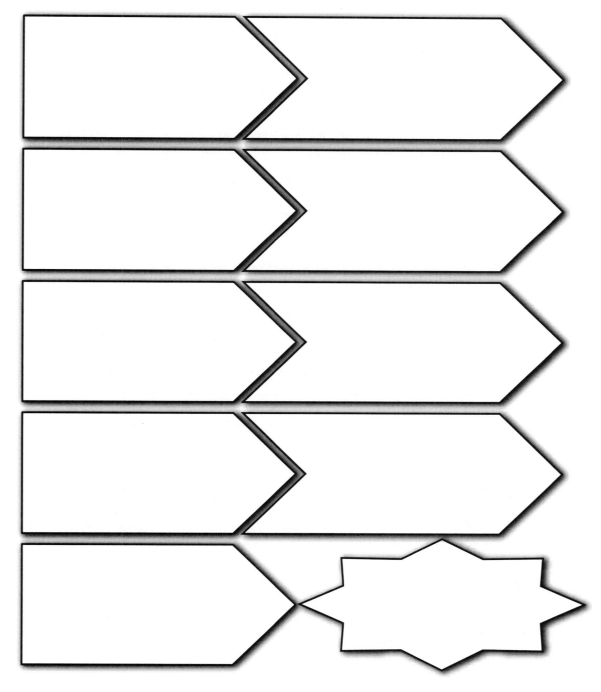

Instructional Manual: How to Fly: Model for a Paper Airplane

Step 1. Choose the right type of paper. It can't be too light (will not get enough *lift*) or too heavy (will create too much *drag*).

Step 2. There are many good paper airplane designs, but the best designs take into account *aerodynamics*. The key is folding a paper airplane with wings that can get *lift* but are not so big that they are out of *balance* and cause the plane to flip, spin, or quickly fall to the ground.

Step 3. Make sure you have crisp folds to help the airplane cut through the air. Paper airplanes have a lot of *potential energy*; the better you make the design, the longer the plane's flight and *hang time* will be.

Step 4. After your design is made, you are not done. The design affects the flight, but the *thrust* you give it also makes a difference. *Thrust* is the forward *momentum* that comes from the *force* you give the plane when you give it a *push* off. In this moment, an *energy transfer* is occurring between you and the plane. This is when your plane shifts from demonstrating *potential energy* to *kinetic energy*.

Step 5. The next step is what it's all about—*lift*. *Lift* is what keeps the paper airplane in the air. As the plane glides, air flows around the wings. The goal is to have more air push up from below the airplane than push down on it. This is why your wing design is so important.

Step 6. As lift begins, so does *drag*. *Drag* is the *resistance* from the air against the plane's forward motion. You can see it slowing down the plane as it soars through the air. This is why the design and weight of the paper are so important. You want to minimize *drag* and increase *lift* to get the longest possible flight.

Step 7. Eventually, the airplane's journey must come to an end because of *gravity*. You can see the *momentum* slowing as the plane plummets toward the ground. The *lift* the plane got fought *gravity* as long as it could. But when it comes to *gravity* and paper airplanes, it's good to know that on Earth *gravity* always wins. *Gravity* is the *force* that *pulls* a paper airplane down to the ground.

Step 8. Learn from what you saw your plane do and make adjustments to try to improve your airplane's *hang time*. With each change, think about what you can do to make the plane more *aerodynamic*. The longer the *hang time*, the more you get to see your plane soar through the air and all of your hard work pay off!

CHAPTER 16

SKIT: NEWTON'S LAWS

Writing Styles

Skit, play

Purpose

Students will work collaboratively to apply knowledge and vocabulary for one of Newton's laws of motion.

Overview

Students show their understanding of one of Newton's laws through a skit.

Language Arts Connections

A skit is written much like a story, with a plot, setting, characters, conflict, and resolution. The organizer provided will help students include those story elements.

Students may need a model of how to write a skit in a play format. They should have the character's name and then a colon followed by the character's speaking line. If there are stage directions, students can write them in italics and parentheses.

Differentiation Strategies

Some students may feel nervous about presenting in front of the class. Therefore, it may help to give those students the option of making a movie. Recording a movie allows students to use their technology skills to enhance the quality of the skit.

Connections to the *Next Generation Science Standards*

- **MS-PS2-1:** Apply Newton's third law to design a solution to a problem involving the motion of two colliding objects.
- **MS-PS3-5:** Construct, use, and present arguments to support the claim that when the kinetic energy of an object changes, energy is transferred to or from the object.
- **HS-PS2-4:** Use mathematical representations of Newton's law of gravitation and Coulomb's law to describe and predict the gravitational and electrostatic forces between objects.

Applications to Other Science Areas

Students could write a skit to show their understanding of symbiotic relationships or forest succession.

Name: _____ Date: _____

Skit: Newton's Laws

Your assignment is to creatively teach the class about one of Newton's laws of motion by performing a skit. Your goal is to show your knowledge and vocabulary from this unit by applying them to a real-life situation.

Vocabulary we could use from this unit in our writing includes the following:

You will be scored according to the following rubric:

AREA	1 DOES NOT MEET EXPECTATIONS	2 PARTIALLY MEETS EXPECTATIONS	3 MEETS EXPECTATIONS	4 EXCEEDS EXPECTATIONS
SCIENCE CONTENT	The skit lacks information and shows that you do not understand the law, or the skit shows consistent misconceptions.	The skit shows correct understanding of the law but lacks details, or the skit demonstrates some minor misconceptions.	The skit includes appropriate and detailed information that shows an overall understanding of the law.	The skit has thorough and detailed information, showing an understanding of the law that is distinguished (very strong).
USE OF SCIENCE VOCABULARY	The skit does not include enough science vocabulary to show understanding, or the skit uses terms incorrectly.	The skit includes some relevant science vocabulary, but it needs more to adequately show knowledge.	The skit consistently uses science vocabulary in the appropriate context.	The skit uses extensive and appropriate science vocabulary throughout.
ORAL PRESENTATION	The skit is unprepared and unclear.	Parts of the skit are unclear because of a lack of organization, volume, or eye contact.	The skit is organized and has consistent eye contact and a clear speaking style.	The skit has the "wow" factor and really captures the class's attention!

Use the organizer on page 110 to plan your story idea.

Name: _____ Date: _____

Skit: Newton's Laws

Your assignment is to creatively teach the class about one of Newton's laws of motion by performing a skit. Your goal is to show your knowledge and vocabulary from this unit by applying them to a real-life situation.

> **Vocabulary we could use from this unit in our writing includes the following:**

You will be scored according to the following rubric:

AREA	1 DOES NOT MEET EXPECTATIONS	2 PARTIALLY MEETS EXPECTATIONS	3 MEETS EXPECTATIONS	4 EXCEEDS EXPECTATIONS
SCIENCE CONTENT	The skit lacks information and shows that you do not understand the law, *or* the skit shows consistent misconceptions.	The skit shows correct understanding of the law but lacks details, *or* the skit demonstrates some minor misconceptions.	The skit includes appropriate and detailed information that shows an overall understanding of the law.	The skit has thorough and detailed information, showing an understanding of the law that is distinguished (very strong).
USE OF SCIENCE VOCABULARY	The skit does not include enough science vocabulary to show understanding, *or* the skit uses terms incorrectly.	The skit includes some relevant science vocabulary, but it needs more to adequately show knowledge.	The skit consistently uses science vocabulary in the appropriate context.	The skit uses extensive and appropriate science vocabulary throughout.
ORAL PRESENTATION	The skit is unprepared and unclear.	Parts of the skit are unclear because of a lack of organization, volume, or eye contact.	The skit is organized and has consistent eye contact and a clear speaking style.	The skit has the "wow" factor and really captures the class's attention!
WRITING FLUENCY	Writing flow and errors in sentence structure make the skit difficult to understand.	Writing flow and errors in sentence structure distract the reader.	The sentence structure is correct, and the flow of writing is smooth to the reader.	The sentence structure, flow, and style of writing are distinguished (very strong).
CONVENTIONS	Spelling, capitalization, and punctuation errors make the skit difficult to understand.	Spelling, capitalization, and punctuation errors distract the reader.	The spelling, capitalization, punctuation, and grammar are mostly *or* all correct.	TThe spelling, capitalization, punctuation, and grammar are distinguished (very strong).

Use the organizer on page 110 to plan your story idea.

CREATIVE WRITING IN SCIENCE

Name: _____ Date: _____

Skit: Newton's Laws: Organizer

Which law will you demonstrate? _____

State this law: _____
_____

What does this law mean in your own words?_____
_____

In one sentence, summarize how you will show this law in a skit:_____
_____
_____
_____

What is the setting of your skit?_____

What is the conflict in your skit?_____
_____

How is the conflict resolved?_____
_____

How does your skit begin?_____
_____

How does your skit end?_____

Who are the characters in your skit, and what are they like?
_____
_____
_____
_____
_____
_____

Skit: Newton's Laws: Model for Newton's First Law

(The setting of the skit is a track. Three runners are stretching, an announcer is nearby, and the students in class represent the crowd watching the event.)

Announcer:	It's almost time for the final round of the 50-meter dash. The three finalists are finding their spots on the start line. (*Runners move to start line.*)
Runner 1:	I can feel all the *potential energy* in me!
Runner 2:	I'm going to go so fast that even *friction* won't slow me down!
Runner 3:	I'm going to *accelerate* past you both!
Announcer:	They are getting in the ready position. (*Runners bend down in the ready position.*) OK, it's almost start time. (*Runners look down, focused.*) On your mark … get set … go! (*No one moves, as if stuck.*) I said go! GO! Run, people, run! (*Runners are still stuck.*)
Runner 1:	(*All runners are in stuck position, only mouths move.*) What's happening?
Runner 2:	We're stuck. My body doesn't want to move.
Runner 3:	Oh no, I've heard of this. It's called …
Runners 1, 2, 3:	*Inertia!*
Announcer:	We appear to have a case of *inertia* here. The runners are staying in their *current state* and won't move until acted on by an *unbalanced force.*
Runners 1, 2, 3:	We need an unbalanced force!
Announcer:	OK, OK, I'm coming! (*Announcer comes with a meter stick in hand and puts the meter stick along all of their backs so he or she is touching all of them.*) OK, get ready, here comes a force! On your mark … get set … go! (*Announcer pushes with great force, and the runners start running straight ahead*). All right, there they go! I'm strong—look how fast they're running! And they're in a near tie as they approach the finish line. The crowd is going wild! Wait, what's this? They aren't stopping!
Runners 1, 2, 3:	Oh no, *inertia!*

Announcer: *Inertia* also means an *object in motion stays in motion unless acted on by an ...*

Runners 1, 2, 3:   (*still running*) *Unbalanced force!*

Announcer: Let's stay tuned folks ... This race may turn into a marathon!

CHAPTER 17

DO I MATTER? WATER'S DIARY

Writing Styles

Narrative, diary

Purpose

Students will work individually to apply knowledge and vocabulary about the states of matter.

Overview

For this activity, students write diary entries from water's perspective to describe what is happening when water is a solid, liquid, and gas. Students should demonstrate their understanding of molecular density and movement in each state.

Language Arts Connections

A diary entry should have strong voice and be written from the first-person point of view. It is a very personal, honest form of writing that has a strong emotional component. Using the literary device of personification, students may want to think of water as a character. For example, the voice may be different if it takes on the persona of a teenager or a wise, old soul that has experienced the water cycle continuously for many years.

Differentiation Strategies

Students could write three diary entries for the three states of matter, or students could write more than three diary entries to give a sense of the various situations water can be in at each stage. Students could also research the water cycle to better understand the ongoing aspect of this cycle.

Students could be challenged to include the fourth state of matter—plasma—or choose something other than water, such as mercury. An element, such as mercury, is developmentally more difficult for students because, unlike water, they do not see the various states of matter for this element in everyday life.

Whenever using personification, you must be aware of student misconceptions. Personification is used as a literary tool to enhance the engagement of the reader. It is important that students understand that water, in any form, does not experience emotions.

Connections to the *Next Generation Science Standards*

- **5-LS2-1:** Develop a model to describe the movement of matter among plants, animals, decomposers, and the environment.

- **MS-PS1-1:** Develop models to describe the atomic composition of simple molecules and extended structures.

- **MS-PS1-4:** Develop a model that predicts and describes changes in particle motion, temperature, and state of a pure substance when thermal energy is added or removed.

- **MS-PS1-5:** Develop and use a model to describe how the total number of atoms does not change in a chemical reaction, and thus mass is conserved.

Applications to Other Science Areas

You could have students write a diary entry from the perspective of a river that is being polluted, a weather event such as a tornado or hurricane, or an endangered species that is losing its habitat.

Name: _____ Date: _____

Do I Matter? Water's Diary

To show your understanding of the three states of matter, write diary entries from water's perspective as it transitions from one state to the next. Be sure to use knowledge and vocabulary from this unit.

Knowledge or vocabulary I could use from this unit in my writing includes the following:		
SOLID **Setting =**_____	**LIQUID** **Setting =**_____	**GAS** **Setting =**_____

You will be scored according to the following rubric:

AREA	1 DOES NOT MEET EXPECTATIONS	2 PARTIALLY MEETS EXPECTATIONS	3 MEETS EXPECTATIONS	4 EXCEEDS EXPECTATIONS
SCIENCE CONTENT	The diary lacks information and shows that you do not understand the states of matter, *or* the diary shows consistent misconceptions.	The diary shows correct understanding of the states of matter but lacks details, *or* the diary demonstrates some minor misconceptions.	The diary includes appropriate and detailed information about the states of matter that shows an overall understanding.	The diary has thorough and detailed information, showing an understanding of the states of matter that is distinguished (very strong).
USE OF SCIENCE VOCABULARY	The diary does not include enough science vocabulary to show understanding, *or* the diary uses terms incorrectly.	The diary includes some relevant science vocabulary, but it needs more to adequately show knowledge.	The diary consistently uses science vocabulary in the appropriate context.	The diary uses extensive and appropriate science vocabulary throughout.

Name: _____ Date: _____

Do I Matter? Water's Diary

To show your understanding of the states of matter, write diary entries from water's perspective as it transitions from one state to the next. Be sure to use knowledge and vocabulary from this unit.

Knowledge or vocabulary I could use from this unit in my writing includes the following:		
SOLID **Setting =**_____	**LIQUID** **Setting =**_____	**GAS** **Setting =**_____

You will be scored according to the following rubric:

AREA	1 DOES NOT MEET EXPECTATIONS	2 PARTIALLY MEETS EXPECTATIONS	3 MEETS EXPECTATIONS	4 EXCEEDS EXPECTATIONS
SCIENCE CONTENT	The diary lacks information and shows that you do not understand the states of matter, or the diary shows consistent misconceptions.	The diary shows correct understanding of the states of matter but lacks details, or the diary demonstrates some minor misconceptions.	The diary includes appropriate and detailed information about the states of matter that shows an overall understanding.	The diary has thorough and detailed information, showing an understanding of the states of matter that is distinguished (very strong).
USE OF SCIENCE VOCABULARY	The diary does not include enough science vocabulary to show understanding, or the diary uses terms incorrectly.	The diary includes some relevant science vocabulary, but it needs more to adequately show knowledge.	The diary consistently uses science vocabulary in the appropriate context.	The diary uses extensive and appropriate science vocabulary throughout.
WRITING FLUENCY	Writing flow and errors in sentence structure make the diary difficult to understand.	Writing flow and errors in sentence structure distract the reader.	The sentence structure is correct, and the flow of writing is smooth to the reader.	The sentence structure, flow, and style of writing are distinguished (very strong).
CONVENTIONS	Spelling, capitalization, and punctuation errors make the diary difficult to understand.	Spelling, capitalization, and punctuation errors distract the reader.	The spelling, capitalization, punctuation, and grammar are mostly or all correct.	TThe spelling, capitalization, punctuation, and grammar are distinguished (very strong).

Do I Matter? Water's Diary: Model for Liquid State

September 21

Dear Diary,

When I am liquid, I am free. My molecules of hydrogen and oxygen have enough room between them that they are *not crowded* and tight. When I am in a liquid state, my molecules are *still touching* and *vibrating*, but they *slide* past each other and it feels like I can go anywhere. I can be rain falling from the sky, a part of the vast sea, or a bit of dew forming on a piece of grass on a warm spring day.

Today was a good day because I rained down from the clouds, through *precipitation*, into a pool. I never know where I'm going to land, but a pool is like a water droplet's trip to paradise. Kids were jumping and splashing and having so much fun. At one point, I clung to the hair of a teenager, then I rejoined the rest of the water in the pool when he tried to make everyone laugh by doing a belly flop off of the diving board. It was pretty funny! When he hit the water, I flew from him all the way to the shallow end. I felt like I was doing a belly flop too as my *molecules* slid and moved!

I wish I could enjoy it all, but I started stressing out as the sun got higher and higher in the sky. I was so afraid that it would get too hot and that I'd be taken away. I hate *evaporation*! It feels like I always turn to *gas* just when I'm having fun. Luckily, that didn't happen. Instead, I met some new friends and felt like I truly fit in with the group!

CHAPTER 18

ENGINEERING EDITORIAL

Writing Styles

Persuasive, argumentative, letter

Purpose

Students will work individually to apply knowledge about an invention's significance in society.

Overview

For this activity, students write a letter to the editor of *Inventors Digest* to explain what they believe to be the most important engineering invention (such as the elevator or the bicycle) or engineering feat (such as the Hoover Dam or the Hubble Telescope). This activity allows students to reflect on the importance that engineering has had in society.

Language Arts Connections

Persuasive or argumentative writing is when you try to convince your audience that your claim is correct. Argumentative writing emphasizes the evidence to support your claim and the acknowledgment of a counterclaim. Persuasive writing includes more emotions and personal opinion; however, it is important that the writing also has evidence to show knowledge. Both forms of writing could be applied to a letter to the editor, depending on the tone that the writer would like to take. If students would like to include more voice and personal opinion, they should be steered toward writing a persuasive piece rather than an argumentative one.

Some students may not know what an editor does at a newspaper or magazine or why people write letters to the editor. Have students look at various examples of letters to the editor to examine both the effectiveness of supporting claims and the writing style. This activity can help students better understand the balance between tone, personal opinion, and evidence.

Because students will need to research information about an invention or engineering design, it may benefit them to learn about the appropriate ways to conduct research and the most reliable forums for gathering information. It may also help students to see how to correctly cite sources.

Differentiation Strategies

It may help students to be given a list of engineering options to choose from. This list could include inventions; the inventor, engineer, or engineering team; and the year that the invention or accomplishment happened.

The prompt could be altered so students write an editorial about a real-world problem that could be solved in the future through engineering and design. Students could speculate about the design aspects that would be most beneficial to solving the problem.

Connections to the *Next Generation Science Standards*

- **3-ETS1-2:** Generate and compare multiple possible solutions to a problem based on how well each is likely to meet the criteria and constraints of the problem.

- **MS-ETS1-2:** Evaluate competing design solutions using a systematic process to determine how well they meet the criteria and constraints of a problem.

- **MS-ETS1-3:** Analyze data from tests to determine similarities and differences among several design solutions to identify the best characteristics of each that can be combined into a new solution to better meet the criteria for success.

- **HS-ETS1-1:** Analyze a major global challenge to specify qualitative and quantitative criteria and constraints for solutions that account for societal needs and wants.

- **HS-ETS1-2:** Design a solution to a complex real-word problem by breaking it down into smaller, more manageable problems that can be solved through engineering.

- **HS-ETS1-3:** Evaluate a solution to a complex real-world problem based on prioritized criteria and trade-offs that account for a range of constraints, including cost, safety, reliability, and aesthetics as well as possible social, cultural, and environmental impacts.

Applications to Other Science Areas

Students could write a letter to the editor or write an editorial about an environmental conservation issue, the use of the metric system around the world, or a genetics topic.

Name: _____ Date: _____

Engineering Editorial

Inventors Digest is seeking opinions about which engineering invention or accomplishment had the most significant positive effect on humans. You will write a letter to the editor of the magazine with your suggestion. Back up your claim with research about the invention or accomplishment, and include evidence of its positive influence.

Invention/Accomplishment:_____

This was designed/created by:_____

in_____

Facts about this invention/accomplishment include the following:

You will be scored according to the following rubric:

AREA	1 DOES NOT MEET EXPECTATIONS	2 PARTIALLY MEETS EXPECTATIONS	3 MEETS EXPECTATIONS	4 EXCEEDS EXPECTATIONS
SCIENCE CONTENT	The letter lacks information and shows that you do not understand the importance of the invention/design, *or* letter shows consistent misconceptions.	The letter shows correct understanding about the importance of the invention/ design but lacks details, *or* letter demonstrates some minor misconceptions.	The letter includes appropriate and detailed information that shows an overall understanding of the invention/design.	The letter has thorough and detailed information about the invention/ design, showing an understanding that is distinguished (very strong).

Use the organizer on page 123 to plan your writing.

Name: _____ Date: _____

Engineering Editorial

Inventors Digest is seeking opinions about which engineering invention or accomplishment had the most significant positive effect on humans. You will write a letter to the editor of the magazine with your suggestion. Back up your claim with research about the invention or accomplishment, and include evidence of its positive influence.

Invention/Accomplishment: _____

This was designed/created by:_____

in_____

Facts about this invention/accomplishment include the following:

You will be scored according to the following rubric:

AREA	1 DOES NOT MEET EXPECTATIONS	2 PARTIALLY MEETS EXPECTATIONS	3 MEETS EXPECTATIONS	4 EXCEEDS EXPECTATIONS
SCIENCE CONTENT	The letter lacks information and shows that you do not understand the importance of the invention/ design, *or* the letter shows consistent misconceptions.	The letter shows correct understanding about the importance of the invention/ design but lacks details, *or* the letter demonstrates some minor misconceptions.	The letter includes appropriate and detailed information that shows an overall understanding of this invention/design.	The letter has thorough and detailed information about the invention/ design, showing an understanding that is distinguished (very strong).
WRITING FLUENCY	Writing flow and errors in sentence structure make the letter difficult to understand.	Writing flow and errors in sentence structure distract the reader.	The sentence structure is correct, and the flow of writing is smooth to the reader.	The sentence structure, flow, and style of writing are distinguished (very strong).
CONVENTIONS	Spelling, capitalization, and punctuation errors make the letter difficult to understand.	Spelling, capitalization, and punctuation errors distract the reader.	The spelling, capitalization, punctuation, and grammar are mostly *or* all correct.	The spelling, capitalization, punctuation, and grammar are distinguished (very strong).

Use the organizer on page 123 to plan your writing.

Name: _____ Date: _____

Engineering Editorial: Organizer

Introduction: Make a *claim* about what you think is the most important engineering invention or accomplishment, and give your most significant reason for its importance.

Body: Include *evidence* of why this invention or accomplishment is important to society.

Conclusion: End with a lasting message about the importance of this invention or engineering accomplishment.

Engineering Editorial: Model for the Printing Press

Dear Editor,

I believe the most important engineering invention, to date, is the printing press. Without the printing press, human civilization would not have the ability to spread ideas and knowledge.

Johannes Gutenberg invented the printing press in 1440, yet most people have never heard of him. His invention was essential to the growth and progress of society for many reasons, but perhaps the most important is the ability to spread ideas quickly. Before his invention, bookmakers had to go through the painstaking process of making books by hand. Imagine how long it would take to write and assemble a 100 page book? Now imagine if you had moveable print and the ability to produce page after page using a press. You would be able to make far more books, at a cheaper cost, which could make the book accessible to many more people.

As a result of this invention, ideas and literacy spread around the world. Knowledge of a range of topics, such as scientific discoveries, religion, and medical advancements were able to travel from person to person quickly and affordably. Without the ability to create books and spread knowledge, where would society be today?

Therefore, I believe that Johannes Gutenberg's name should be said with the same regard as inventors such as Thomas Edison and Benjamin Franklin. For without Gutenberg's press, the accomplishments of Edison and Franklin may never have been shared with the world.

Sincerely,

_____

APPENDIXES

APPENDIX 1

CONNECTIONS TO *COMMON CORE STATE STANDARDS* FOR WRITING AND FOR SPEAKING AND LISTENING

The tables on the following pages indicate the *Common Core State Standards* (*CCSS*) for writing and for speaking and listening covered in each chapter.

Grades 3–5 *CCSS* for Writing and for Speaking and Listening

GRADE 3	W 3.1	W 3.1 A	W 3.1 B	W 3.1 C	W 3.1 D	W 3.2	W 3.2 A	W 3.2 B	W 3.2 C	W 3.2 D	X	W 3.3	W 3.3 A	W 3.3 B	W 3.3 C	W 3.3 D	W 3.4	X	S 3.4	X
GRADE 4	W 4.1	W 4.1 A	W 4.1 B	W 4.1 C	W 4.1 D	W 4.2	W 4.2 A	W 4.2 B	W 4.2 C	W 4.2 D	W 4.2 E	W 4.3	W 4.3 A	W 4.3 B	W 4.3 C	W 4.3 D	W 4.3 E	W 4.4	S 4.4	X
GRADE 5	W 5.1	W 5.1 A	W 5.1 B	W 5.1 C	W 5.1 D	W 5.2	W 5.2 A	W 5.2 B	W 5.2 C	W 5.2 D	W 5.2 E	W 5.3	W 5.3 A	W 5.3 B	W 5.3 C	W 5.3 D	W 5.3 E	W 5.4	S 5.4	S 5.6
EVERY TREE IS A CHARACTER						*	*	*	*	*	*	*	*	*	*	*	*	*		
POSTCARD FROM A BIOME						*	*	*	*	*	*	*	*	*	*	*	*	*		
TRAVEL BLOG ABOUT THE DIGESTIVE SYSTEM						*	*	*	*	*	*	*	*	*	*	*	*	*		
PHYTOPLANKTON COMIC						*	*	*		*	*	*	*			*	*	*		
MOTIVATIONAL SPEECH BY A PART OF A CELL	*	*	*	*	*	*	*	*	*	*	*	*	*	*	*	*	*	*	*	*
GROUP POEM: EARTH'S HISTORY						*	*	*	*	*	*	*	*	*	*	*	*	*	*	*
PRESENTING ... THE ROCK CYCLE!						*	*	*				*	*	*			*	*	*	*
SCI-FI: WHAT WOULD THE WORLD BE LIKE IF THE KT ASTEROID HAD NEVER HIT?	*	*	*	*	*	*	*	*	*	*	*	*	*	*	*	*	*	*		
PACKING LIST FOR THE PLANETS	*	*	*	*	*	*	*	*	*	*	*	*		*		*	*	*		
LETTER FROM THE MOON TO EARTH	*	*	*	*	*	*	*	*	*	*	*	*	*	*	*	*	*	*		
INTERVIEW WITH AN ATOM						*	*	*	*	*	*	*	*	*	*	*	*	*	*	*
INSTRUCTIONAL MANUAL: HOW TO FLY	*	*	*	*	*	*	*	*	*	*	*	*	*	*	*	*	*	*		
SKIT: NEWTON'S LAWS						*	*	*	*	*	*	*	*	*	*	*	*	*	*	*
DO I MATTER? WATER'S DIARY						*	*	*	*	*	*	*	*	*	*	*	*	*		
ENGINEERING EDITORIAL	*	*	*	*	*	*	*	*	*	*	*	*	*	*	*	*	*	*		

Grades 6–8 *CCSS* for Writing and for Speaking and Listening

	W6.1	W6.1A	W6.1B	W6.1C	W6.1D	W6.1E	W6.2	W6.2A	W6.2B	W6.2C	W6.2D	W6.2E	W6.2F	W6.3	W6.3A	W6.3B	W6.3C	W6.3D	W6.3E	W6.4	S6.4	S6.6
GRADE 6	W6.1	W6.1A	W6.1B	W6.1C	W6.1D	W6.1E	W6.2	W6.2A	W6.2B	W6.2C	W6.2D	W6.2E	W6.2F	W6.3	W6.3A	W6.3B	W6.3C	W6.3D	W6.3E	W6.4	S6.4	S6.6
GRADE 7	W7.1	W7.1A	W7.1B	W7.1C	W7.1D	W7.1E	W7.2	W7.2A	W7.2B	W7.2C	W7.2D	W7.2E	W7.2F	W7.3	W7.3A	W7.3B	W7.3C	W7.3D	W7.3E	W7.4	S7.4	S7.6
GRADE 8	W8.1	W8.1A	W8.1B	W8.1C	W8.1D	W8.1E	W8.2	W8.2A	W8.2B	W8.2C	W8.2D	W8.2E	W8.2F	W8.3	W8.3A	W8.3B	W8.3C	W8.3D	W8.3E	W8.4	S8.4	S8.6
EVERY TREE IS A CHARACTER							*	*	*	*	*	*	*	*	*	*	*	*	*	*		
POSTCARD FROM A BIOME							*	*	*	*	*	*	*	*	*	*	*	*	*	*		
TRAVEL BLOG ABOUT THE DIGESTIVE SYSTEM							*	*	*	*	*	*	*	*	*	*	*	*	*	*		
PHYTOPLANKTON COMIC							*	*	*		*		*	*	*	*		*	*	*		
MOTIVATIONAL SPEECH BY A PART OF A CELL	*	*	*	*	*	*	*	*	*	*	*	*	*	*	*	*	*	*	*	*	*	*
GROUP POEM: EARTH'S HISTORY							*	*	*	*	*	*	*	*	*	*		*	*	*	*	*
PRESENTING ... THE ROCK CYCLE!							*	*	*	*	*	*	*	*	*	*	*	*	*	*	*	*
SCI-FI: WHAT WOULD THE WORLD BE LIKE IF THE KT ASTEROID HAD NEVER HIT?	*	*	*	*	*	*	*	*	*	*	*	*	*	*	*	*	*	*	*	*		
PACKING LIST FOR THE PLANETS	*	*	*	*	*	*	*	*	*	*	*	*	*	*	*		*	*	*	*		
LETTER FROM THE MOON TO EARTH	*	*	*	*	*	*	*	*	*	*	*	*	*	*	*	*	*	*	*	*		
INTERVIEW WITH AN ATOM							*	*	*	*	*	*	*	*	*	*	*	*	*	*	*	*
INSTRUCTIONAL MANUAL: HOW TO FLY	*	*	*	*	*	*	*	*	*	*	*	*	*	*	*	*	*	*	*	*		
SKIT: NEWTON'S LAWS							*	*	*	*	*	*	*	*	*	*	*	*	*	*	*	*
DO I MATTER? WATER'S DIARY							*	*	*	*	*	*	*	*	*	*	*	*	*	*		
ENGINEERING EDITORIAL	*	*	*	*	*	*	*	*	*	*	*	*	*	*	*	*	*	*	*	*		

Grades 9–12 *CCSS* for Writing and for Speaking and Listening

	W.1	W.1A	W.1B	W.1C	W.1D	W.1E	W.2	W.2A	W.2B	W.2C	W.2D	W.2E	W.2F	W.3	W.3A	W.3B	W.3C	W.3D	W.3E	W.4	S.4	S.6
GRADES 9–10	W.1	W.1A	W.1B	W.1C	W.1D	W.1E	W.2	W.2A	W.2B	W.2C	W.2D	W.2E	W.2F	W.3	W.3A	W.3B	W.3C	W.3D	W.3E	W.4	S.4	S.6
GRADES 11–12	W.1	W.1A	W.1B	W.1C	W.1D	W.1E	W.2	W.2A	W.2B	W.2C	W.2D	W.2E	W.2F	W.3	W.3A	W.3B	W.3C	W.3D	W.3E	W.4	S.4	S.6
EVERY TREE IS A CHARACTER							*	*	*	*	*	*	*	*	*	*	*	*	*	*		
POSTCARD FROM A BIOME							*	*	*	*	*	*	*	*	*	*	*	*	*	*		
TRAVEL BLOG ABOUT THE DIGESTIVE SYSTEM							*	*	*	*	*	*	*	*	*	*	*	*	*	*		
PHYTOPLANKTON COMIC							*	*	*		*		*	*	*	*	*	*	*	*		
MOTIVATIONAL SPEECH BY A PART OF A CELL	*	*	*	*	*	*	*	*	*	*	*	*	*	*	*	*	*	*	*	*	*	*
GROUP POEM: EARTH'S HISTORY							*	*	*	*	*	*	*	*	*	*	*	*	*	*	*	*
PRESENTING ... THE ROCK CYCLE!							*	*	*		*	*	*	*		*	*	*	*	*	*	*
SCI-FI: WHAT WOULD THE WORLD BE LIKE IF THE KT ASTEROID HAD NEVER HIT?	*	*	*	*	*	*	*	*	*	*	*	*	*	*	*	*	*	*	*	*		
PACKING LIST FOR THE PLANETS	*	*	*	*	*	*	*	*	*		*	*	*	*		*		*	*	*		
LETTER FROM THE MOON TO EARTH	*	*	*	*	*	*	*	*	*	*	*	*	*	*	*	*	*	*	*	*		
INTERVIEW WITH AN ATOM							*	*	*	*	*	*	*	*	*	*	*	*	*	*	*	*
INSTRUCTIONAL MANUAL: HOW TO FLY	*	*	*	*	*	*	*	*	*	*	*	*	*	*	*	*	*	*	*	*		
SKIT: NEWTON'S LAWS							*	*	*	*	*	*	*	*	*	*	*	*	*	*	*	*
DO I MATTER? WATER'S DIARY							*	*	*	*	*	*	*	*	*	*	*	*	*	*		
ENGINEERING EDITORIAL	*	*	*	*	*	*	*	*	*	*	*	*	*	*	*	*	*	*	*	*		

APPENDIX 2

RESOURCES

Standards

National Governors Association Center for Best Practices and Council of Chief State School Officers (NGAC and CCSSO). 2010. *Common core state standards.* Washington, DC: NGAC and CCSSO.

NGSS Lead States. 2013. *Next Generation Science Standards: For states, by states.* Washington, DC: National Academies Press. *www.nextgenscience.org/next-generation-science-standards.*

Every Tree Is a Character

Longley, S. 2005. Wood hardness chart. The Workshop Pages. *http://workshoppages.com/WS/Misc/Wood-Hardness-Chart.pdf.*

New York State Department of Environmental Conservation. 2005. Beavers in the food chain. *www.dec.ny.gov/docs/administration_pdf/2005jrnat4.pdf.*

Pennsylvania Woodlands. 2015. *www.ltsd.k12.pa.us/cms/lib04/PA06000061/Centricity/Domain/169/PAWoodlandsForestTerminologyNumber4.pdf.*

Project Learning Tree. *www.plt.org.*

SavA Tree. 2015. Birch tree care, pruning tips, signs of diseases or other problems. *www.savatree.com/birch-tree.html.*

Wikipedia. 2015. Climax species. *http://en.wikipedia.org/wiki/Climax_species.*

Postcard From a Biome

Blue Planet Biomes. 2001. Tropical rainforest. *www.blueplanetbiomes.org/rainforest.htm.*

National Geographic. 1996. Rain forest at night. National Geographic Society. *www.nationalgeographic.com/features/00/earthpulse/rainforest/gallery1.html.*

The Living Rainforest. 2015. The high life: Epiphytes. *www.livingrainforest.org/about-rainforests/the-high-life-epiphytes.*

World Wide Metric. 2015. Measurements. *www.worldwidemetric.com/measurements.html.*

Travel Blog About the Digestive System

Bailey, R. 2015. Digestive system: Nutrient absorption. About Education. *http://biology.about.com/od/organsystems/a/aa032907a.htm.*

Cleveland Clinic Foundation. 2013. Diseases and conditions: Digestive system. *http://my.clevelandclinic.org/health/diseases_conditions/hic_The_Structure_and_Function_of_the_Digestive_System.*

Encyclopedia Britannica. 2014a. Chyme. *www.britannica.com/EBchecked/topic/117464/chyme.*

Encyclopedia Britannica. 2014b. Peristalsis. *www.britannica.com/EBchecked/topic/452053/peristalsis.*

Encyclopedia Britannica. 2015. Cilium. *www.britannica.com/EBchecked/topic/117814/cilium.*

Molecular & Cell Biology. 2015. *The Digestive System. https://mcb.berkeley.edu/courses/mcb32/Miller%20 notes-%20digestive%20system%20.*

National Institute of Diabetes and Digestive and Kidney Diseases. 2013. Your digestive system and how it works. National Institutes of Health. *www.niddk.nih.gov/health-information/health-topics/Anatomy/your-digestive-system/Pages/anatomy.aspx.*

Paul, I. 2015. Digestive system. Biology Reference. *www.biologyreference.com/Co-Dn/Digestive-System.html.*

Picco, M. F. 2012. Digestion: How long does it take? Mayo Clinic. *www.mayoclinic.org/digestive-system/experty-answers/faq-20058340.*

WebMD. 2014. Digestive Disorders Health Center. *www.webmd.com/digestive-disorders/digestive-system.*

Zimmermann, K. A. 2015. Digestive system: Facts, function, and diseases. Live Science. *www.livescience.com/22367-digestive-system.html.*

Phytoplankton Comic

Bird, J. 1999. Plankton: Ocean drifters. Oceanic Research Group. *www.oceanicresearch.org/education/films/planktonscript.htm.*

Hansen, A. 2011. Invisible watery world. Arizona State University School of Life Sciences. *http://askabiologist.asu.edu/explore/plankton.*

National Oceanic and Atmospheric Administration. 2014. What are phytoplankton? *http://oceanservice.noaa.gov/facts/phyto.html.*

Motivational Speech by a Part of a Cell

Andrew Rader Studio. 2015. Cell wall—What's it for? Biology4Kids. *www.biology4kids.com/files/cell_wall.html.*

Wikipedia. 2015. Cell wall. *http://en.wikipedia.org/wiki/Cell_wall.*

Group Poem: Earth's History

British Broadcasting Corporation. 2015. NATURE prehistoric life: History of life on Earth. *www.bbc.co.uk/nature/history_of_the_earth*.

International Commission on Stratigraphy. *www.stratigraphy.org*.

National Geographic. 2015. Precambrian time. National Geographic Society. *http://science. nationalgeographic.com/science/prehistoric-world/precambrian*.

Polly, D. 2011. The Mesozoic Era. University of California Museum of Paleontology. *www.ucmp. berkeley.edu/mesozoic/mesozoic.php*.

Wikipedia. 2015. Precambrian. *http://en.wikipedia.org/wiki/Precambrian*.

Presenting ... the Rock Cycle!

University of Maryland. 2015. The rock cycle and igneous rocks I. *www.geol.umd.edu/~jmerck/ geol100/lectures/10.html*.

Sci-Fi: What Would the World Be Like If the KT Asteroid Had Never Hit?

Castro, J. 2014. Tyrannosaurus rex: Facts about T. rex, king of the dinosaurs. Live Science. *www. livescience.com/23868-tyrannosaurus-rex-facts.html*.

Wikipedia. 2015. Tyrannosaurus. *http://en.wikipedia.org/wiki/Tyrannosaurus*.

Packing List for the Planets

National Geographic. 2015a. Mercury. National Geographic Society. *http://science.nationalgeographic. com/science/space/solar-system/mercury-article*.

National Geographic. 2015b. Voyager: The interstellar mission. National Geographic Society. *http://voyager.jpl.nasa.gov/science/neptune.html*.

PlanetFacts.org. 2015. Planet Mercury facts. *http://planetfacts.org/planet-mercury-facts*.

The Planets. 2015. Distances between planets. *http://theplanets.org/distances-between-planets*.

Redd, N. T. 2015. How hot is Mercury? Space.com. *www.space.com/18645-mercury-temperature.html*.

Letter From the Moon to Earth

National Aeronautics and Space Administration. 2015. *Solar system exploration. http://solarsystem. nasa.gov/planets/profile.cfm?Display=Facts&Object=Moon*.

National Oceanic and Atmospheric Administration. 2013. Tides and currents: Detailed explanation of the differential tide producing forces. *http://tidesandcurrents.noaa.gov/restles3.html*.

WikiHow. 2015. How to write a formal letter. *www.wikihow.com/Write-a-Formal-Letter*.

Interview With an Atom

Chemicool. 2015. Alphabetical elements list. *www.chemicool.com/elements*.

Chem4Kids.com. 2015a. *Bonding basics. www.chem4kids.com/files/atom_bonds.html*.

Chem4Kids.com. 2015b. *Atoms around us. www.chem4kids.com/files/atom_intro.html*.

Dallas Learning Solutions. 2015. The chemistry of life: Chemical bonding. *https://dlc.dcccd.edu/biology1-2/chemical-bonding*.

Morton Salt. 2015. Fun facts. *www.mortonsalt.com/salt-facts/fun-facts*.

Instructional Manual: How to Fly

Aviation for Kids. 2015. Paper airplanes. *www.aviation-for-kids.com/paper-airplanes.html*.

Scholastic. 2015. What makes paper airplanes fly? *www.scholastic.com/teachers/article/what-makes-paper-airplanes-fly*.

Skit: Newton's Laws

Forbus, K. 2015. Propulsion. Northwestern University Qualitative Reasoning Group. *www.qrg.northwestern.edu/projects/vss/docs/propulsion/2-what-is-inertia.html*.

Engineering Editorial

Wolchover, N. 2012. Top 10 inventions that changed the world. Live Science. *www.livescience.com/33749-top-10-inventions-changed-world.html*.

Wikipedia. 2015. Johannes Gutenberg. *http://en.wikipedia.org/wiki/Johannes_Gutenberg*.

INDEX

Page numbers in **boldface** type refer to tables.

INDEX

INDEX